To everyone who has made this journey worth sharing

Welcome

we're Kit & J.R.

We moved into our bus Sunshine in 2012, seeking balance between work and play. On the road, we've developed a philosophical structure by which we live. We call it our Idle Theory. Join us on a wild ride across America, exploring work, leisure, and of course idleness, through the high altitudes of the mind.

get on the bus

www.IdleTheoryBus.com

@IdleTheoryBus

@IdleTheoryBus

Orange is Optimism

KIT WHISTLER & J.R. SWITCHGRASS

AKA

RACHEL GOLDFARB

AKA

JAMES CAMPBELL

First Edition
November 2016
First Printing of 2,000 Books

All Content Written, Photographed, Illustrated, Designed and Typeset by
Kit Whistler & J.R. Switchgrass

Words and Illustrations © Kit Whistler
www.KitWhistler.com

Photographs © J.R. Switchgrass
www.JRSwitchgrass.com

To order
www.OrangeIsOptimism.com

Published by
Wrinkled Trousers LLC
www.WrinkledTrousers.com

ISBN #978-0-9981823-0-8

Printed in the U.S.A. on U.S.A. Manufactured Materials
by Bang Printing, Brainerd, MN

A Note On Authenticity

If you came to this book seeking truth, perhaps you're better off reading a different book. Come to think of it, you should probably avoid books altogether.

Preface

It's a cloudy fall day on the plains of Montana. J.R. and I are sitting in the bus, finalizing the book you now hold in your hands.

It's November, four years to the day since we hit the open roads of America. Isn't it something that the anniversary of that day coincides perfectly with the printing of this book? I think so.

Orange is Optimism was created on the road, for the road, and in tribute to all the tramps and ramblers and hobos who wander its curves and corners.

We brainstormed in the Appalachians. We outlined on the shores of Lake Superior. We wrote in Saskatchewan and Montana and designed in the vast Wyoming Basin, where the wind blew until the bus rumbled.

The bus was our studio, and we wrote to the call of coyotes and the rain pitter pattering on the windows.

This book is about the road. It's also about truth. It's also about how we humans interact with the wild. I truly hope these ideas spark a flame of passion in your soul.

When we began to relate our story on the internet, we were motivated by a desire to share what we learned from the wisdom of the road and the ways of the natural world. Creating a book was a logical step forward, a natural progression to express our thoughts in a long-form way, deeper than the internet allows.

Orange is Optimism is a **Pictotext**, a blend between a novel and a photo book. It's a book for the digital age, containing a coherent collection of stories and photos from the road.

Feel free to read it in the traditional linear fashion, following the plot, or out of sequence as a collection of short stories. Experience it as you wish; remember, you bring just as much to the book as the book brings to you.

J.R. and I collaborate from different fields, mine being word-based and his grounded in image. We've spent a lot of time and effort exploring how our two art forms layer upon each other to create a new, synergistic medium of their own. That is the main purpose of the Pictotext, to explore philosophy and aesthetics through interwoven photographs and literary text.

It's true that *Orange is Optimism* features moments from our lives, but our lifestyle isn't the point. When sharing, it's always been our goal not to glorify a lifestyle, but to discuss ideas that are pertinent to any lifestyle.

We hope you find in these pages philosophy that is relevant to you, that inspires you to see the impossible beauty in all around you.

Obviously, seeking doesn't require living on the road. It was never our intent to create a book to inspire others to live in a van.

What we wanted was to share ideas about work, leisure, and idleness. We wanted to discuss the beauty of the natural world and the role of the wild in human life.

We wanted to ask you if you walk out your front door and give thanks for what the world offers, if you're gaining some semblance of Sanity right where you sit. It's not about living in a van or traveling. It's about seeking.

In curating *Orange is Optimism*, our goal was to share the joys of living a life that's truly alive.

A note on the title. Yes, I know Voltaire well. I used to meet him for coffee every Friday at 10 a.m. We were good friends. That is, until I told him I identified with Candide and he told me I was a fool. Our coffee dates ended shortly after.

Here's the thing: I believe in Optimism.

I believe that the world is an abundant place. I believe the world is always offering its best to us. People are going to tell you to be realistic. But living a beautiful life is not realistic! It's not. So, if you're a realist, take warning. You probably will not enjoy this book.

I can't help but say the world's a wonderful place. I'm just being honest. I truly think it is. I think Voltaire was wrong.

I'm much better friends with Leibniz now. He's a dreamer. If that makes him a fool, so be it. I am too, then. Let us celebrate the foolish, for they are the ones who transform the impossible into the possible.

With the release of *Orange is Optimism*, we foolish dreamers celebrate. But it's not over.

We have many other projects up our sleeves. Many more roads to follow.

We can't wait to live it all, share it all, laugh and cry and touch all of the gorgeous things around us. After all, what's life without anticipation? We plan to continue living out here on the road, working for money when we need to, creating art, and constantly, constantly learning.

For now, that's all we want. We'll chase another rainbow over the next hill, just for a glimpse of somewhere new, until we've seen every new place there is to see.

Earlier today, three coyotes howled outside the bus, and the electricity of their energy still sparks my being.

Please, come and live it with us.

Thank you all for being part of this journey.
Much Love + Orange is Optimism

-Kit

November 2016
Open Road, Anywhere USA

Orange is Optimism

Magic
bursts from
Every
CORNER
of reality.

QUEEN OF NOWHERE

I'm someone everyone should know.

I'm a lost child of America. That's what they say about me, anyway.

Freedom is my sister. That's what *I* say about me, and it's the damn truth.

For formal introductions, they call me Kit. I've been traveling the open road with my pal J.R. for over four years now. We live in an orange VW Bus named Sunshine. That one, there, under those tulip poplars.

J.R. and I travel every day of the year, hot or cold, wind-ridden or pushed out by heavy rain. We seek nothing but find everything, beauty and wonder and the next job to fuel our hungry bellies. We go all over the place. Come to think of it, I can't remember the last time we woke up in the same spot two nights in a row.

You can call us bums, if you want. Personally, I prefer the term "seeker." It has a certain dignity to it, and dignity is something I believe in. I like what's rare. You might say I'm a collector of endangered concepts, a bum who enjoys philosophy.

Yeah, we bums still exist. Maybe if you called us seekers you'd know that. Some simple civilians think the term went out of fashion a long time ago. But we bums are making do. You probably haven't seen us, living on the peripheries of America's strip mall jungles as we do. It's dangerous back there in society, and we're skilled at hiding out from danger. Naw, bums aren't extinct. We're merely camouflaged in our quests for secrecy.

Yeah, I'm a girl. What's that to you? Girls are free to ramble, just as much as the boys. Now, I know that by looking at the history of the bum you'd think that wasn't true. I know that if you'd look through this book, you'd think girls stayed off the open roads.

Not true. There are some of us brave and depraved girls who haven't taken a proper scrubbing to their skin in two months, who can butcher a bird if need be, who pee squatting down, who dig a hole in the dirt six inches deep and call it a toilet. There are some girls like me, hairy legs sticking out of their miniskirts and ecstasy for life blazing from their eyes, who love the roads of America better than they love themselves.

Do I want a Career? Hell, no. Upward mobility? I'm not sure if America's up there at the top. If she is, I'm sure she'll come back down to visit with me.

People tell me that this life I'm building is unrealistic. Apparently realism is all the rage now. They tell me I'm not allowed to have faith in magic. "Describe the world as it is," they say. But I *do* describe the world as it is. I do! I write that the day is too beautiful to be true, they say. But what they don't understand is that the world *is* too beautiful to be true.

You see, there's nothing realistic about living a beautiful life. Beauty is a dreamer's game and dreaming's sort of my speciality. I believe in the impossible and if you're not willing to dream, then good luck to you.

I believe that the universe is always offering its best to us. That makes me an Optimist and, you know, I do believe in the optimal abundance of the natural world. Do you understand? I hope you do, because I'm not quite sure how to explain it any better. Also, I'd like to begin the story you came here for, so I guess I will, right now.

It was an early yawning dawn. We were camped twenty miles down a dirt road. The morning was tender as the new shoots of spring grasses. J.R fried eggs on our two-burner stove, naked. I was naked, too, just letting the skin air out, you know? I'd always thought that too many clothes could strangle a wild soul.

"Morning's here again," I told J.R. "Nothing to do besides watch the rhododendrons open their flowers or discuss the finer points of ontology."

"Kit, you hold your horses. Nothing like that till I've had my first cigarette." J.R. was taking up smoking and having a tough time of it, the poor guy.

Me, I was queen of that forest scene. I liked it there, where no one could find me, in the thick woods of nowhere. Actually, that's exactly what I felt like, the Queen of Nowhere. I surveyed our kingdom, beaming with pride.

J.R. and I, we had our kitchen downstairs in the bus and our bed in the pop top. We had a dirt pad as a front porch, and a strand of ferns as a garden. The call of the Carolina wren was the music on our radio and the wet canopy of trees above served as a fine roof for our patio.

Earlier that day, we'd fetched our drinking water from the creek that pinged past a cluster of cedars. That night, we'd sleep to the chorus of the crickets. This was all I had ever wanted, to live uninhibited and unfettered in places where no one would ask me questions, where I could do and say what I pleased, where no one knew me and the world was wide open for the taking. In the distant past, I used to learn about the world from Walt Whitman. Now, I'd learn from the wisdom of the open road.

Royal as they were, my thoughts were interrupted by a strange sight indeed. A brand-new hatchback approached our temporary kingdom, the first people to pass our nowhere camp in two days.

Two expensive mountain bikes sat stately as chariots on the rack above the shiny car. Their handlebars snorted like horses. The young couple in the hatchback stared over, curious. 'Course they were. Curious, just like us. They must've come out here for the same good reasons we did. They must've been seekers as well. I wrapped one of our soggy blankets around my naked body and ran to their car, a wilderness crossing guard with the loveliest intentions.

"Welcome to our little corner of the woods! I believe that my compadre J.R. is currently brewing coffee. Would you join us for a morning elixir?"

The couple glanced from my face to Sunshine to J.R.'s naked body, which he hadn't bothered to cover because breakfast might burn. They were tense, like I'd invited them to break some law in front of the courthouse. No hello, which I found a little rude, but hey, some people are shy.

"Don't worry!" I said. "I wouldn't invite you over if I didn't mean it."

The driver finally broke his silence. "No, we're afraid——"

"Don't be afraid! We haven't seen any police or bears or anything at all you'd need to be concerned about. Actually—" I held up a finger. "If you need to pee, there are some rusty nails buried in the fallen leaves. If you wear shoes, there's no problem. Come on over."

"No," he said. "We have work to do this afternoon. Saturday mornings, we reserve one hour for mountain biking, then we go back to work. And this morning, I'm afraid we're late." They disappeared down the road, to that somewhere in the woods you could be late to. I returned to J.R.

"Weird! What kind of thing is that to be afraid of, being late?"

"People are rich in things but poor in time," J.R. said, serving up coffee and eggs.

"They have no reason to go back to work. They said it was Saturday. Is that true?"

"Guess we'll have to take their word for it."

I paced back and forth. "I just don't get it! Everyone in society is sick with the work plague. I should've told those hatchback doubters about idle theory."

"Naw, Kit. You gotta change the world by changing yourself. Anything bigger than that is just politics."

His face twisted around like a revolving door as he took a drag on his cigarette.

J.R. was right. Politics is something we steer real clear of. We decided four years back to forgo politics and take our quest for happiness into our own hands. We quit working sixty, eighty, a hundred hours a week. We shed most of our stuff. We set out to find something that's rare in our modern world. We set out to find Sanity.

"Those people are insane," I told J.R. "Using work to justify their existence!"

"I guess we all need a reason to exist," he said.

We sat on the side of the bus, gazing out over the Appalachian Mountains, the consquences of history chiseled into their rounded blue ridges. We listened to the wisdom of those grandfather mountains, no more than hills, really, smoothed down from weather and water, all that tumult doled out by the sky.

I knew we'd savor this view most of the day, blissfully doing nothing. Not like those pessimists, rushing into the woods for an hour-long retreat from their work.

Why, they ran off so fast they didn't notice all the marvelous magical things that happen out here. They missed the call of the cardinal, the verdant smell of the ferns. They even missed America down by the creek, dipping her hair into its cold waters. That was always the way of the Pessimist. Surviving in the midst of scarcity.

Now, you've gotta listen to me, dear reader, and listen good. When someone tells you that work is the noblest virtue, when they insist that idleness is the blackest evil, you've gotta promise me you'll never trust them. People like that are full of pretense. They'll never understand the wisdom of the bum. No one needs to justify their existence with work. No one! That's the whole beauty of this journey called life! The most transcendental gifts are always absolutely free.

Like that pretty morning in our nowhere camp. That was the way to live, the clean air, the song of warblers and vireos that painted the morning orange. All of it belonged to us, even if only for one day. And think! All of it was free of charge, supplied by the generous economy of nature. I wouldn't ever give up this life, not for anything, because in a world of unrealistic miracles, certainty is such a drag. ◊

the Road chants
a rhythmic meditation
a subliminal music
of its own

it pulls us on
Fast as we can go
to who knows where
& who cares where
anyhow

FREEDOM WEARS DRIVING GLOVES

On a cool spring day that smelled like sea salt and the slight breath of a hummingbird, J.R. and I realized the world had gone mad. We looked deep into our surroundings, and the deeper we looked, the more insane everything seemed.

Now, I don't intend to say that the world had gone mad before our very eyes. It's likely that Insanity, who we'd just met, was as old as civilization itself. She probably arrived here on planet Earth about the time agricultural surplus came into existence. Somehow, we'd never noticed her before.

Overnight, she was everywhere, sipping cappuccinos in the corner coffee shop and lecturing at universities. Her name was in the byline of every article in every newspaper I read. She mediated the shows that blabbered on TV and installed billboard advertising along the freeways. She'd even gotten involved in my personal life. Without J.R. or I noticing, and she filled our apartment with so much stuff we could barely walk around.

A productive member of society she was. Busy all the time, just like us. At the time, you see, J.R. and I were living in some megacity, working hard to achieve things we weren't even sure we wanted. We worked forty, sixty, eighty hours a week.

I was under the assumption that work was the most dignified way to express my humanity. Yes, dear reader, laugh if you wish. What a fool I was! I exalted the spirit of work. I was a freak for its accolades. I worshipped in its bank-chain cathedrals.

The devout addict I was, I devoted every moment I could to my beloved occupation. I never pursued leisure. I never ever considered idleness. To me, idleness was filthy, and doing nothing was the worst crime you could commit.

Yeah, I used to believe all that baloney. That's exactly what Insanity does to a soul. My madness was never more apparent than when I sat in my studio apartment, complaining about my studio apartment. Or when I worshipped my job, all the while complaining about my job. Or when I bought stuff and complained about how I was forced to buy stuff I didn't want to buy.

Now that J.R. and I were fully aware of our own madness, what would we do? Was this our lot in life, to trudge forward in the megacity of madness, wallowing in our own Insanity?

One day over corndogs, we decided that wallowing wasn't doing us a bit of good. Those late night complaining sessions had lost their appeal. We were bored. Boredom, we were realizing, was the most acute symptom of Insanity. So, after a good cry and a catastrophic mustard spill, we set out to banish it from our lives.

Seeing as the trappings of Insanity were a pattern of thought, it was obvious we'd have to develop a new ideology in order to reach our goal.

It took awhile, but we developed a set of principles that were sound. We named the resulting philosophy Idle Theory, and it is by the tenets of Idle Theory that we now live. According to our Idle Theory, time was divided into three categories:

1. Work: Time spent in the mode of survival. In modern society: making money.
2. Leisure: Time spent pursuing passions, unmotivated by extrinsic factors.
3. Idleness: Time spent doing nothing. The holiest time there is.

Now that we have that straight, let's get to the meat of it. Our hypothesis, as stated by Idle Theory, was simple, really. We figured that if we devoted less time to work and more time to pursuing leisure and idleness, we would find Sanity.

Yeah, Sanity still exists. It's true, her presence in the world has diminished greatly, especially since the Industrial Revolution and the cruel imperialism of Insanity. Insanity has popularized the misconception that work is humanity's greatest virtue. That myth ran Sanity off into nowhere.

You see, Sanity's sort of like an elk or a wolf. When civilization closes in, she takes refuge in marginal land. She's in the lonely mountains. She winters in the vast deserts. If you've got a clear view of the Milky Way, if there's no traffic noise polluting the still silence of space around you, you're bound to be close to Sanity.

Any search for Sanity takes her seekers to all those wild places, and J.R. and I weren't worried about that one bit. In fact, quite the opposite. We carried our anticipation like a torch. What worried us was the growing likelihood that we'd become bums. For some reason, bums were the only ones searching for Sanity. That scared us a little.

You see, bums don't have a good reputation, because they practice Idle Theory and Idle Theory is society's worst enemy. Bums know better than anyone else that too much work rots the soul and dulls the natural morality within us all. They practice their right to be lazy. They forgo an eighty-hour work week.

Lots of bums say that idleness was common at one time, that people used to live with less and call that living. We bums keep that tradition alive. We believe that Idle Theory will return Sanity to her rightful place in the center of society.

Back in the land of Insanity, it all happened pretty quickly. We didn't really make a plan. There wasn't a period of analysis, no critical thinking involved. We were fueled by something that transcended the need for a good plan, and that something was passion.

We burned for a way out. Our desire ran so deep, it seared holes into our brains. We decided we would flee the city of Insanity. We decided we would move to Sanity's wild cathedrals. She wasn't around the city, that much was for sure.

First off, I quit that job I hated. My boss asked why and I told him I realized I didn't want most of the things I could buy with the money I earned.

"You're Insane," he said.

"I know!" I responded. "That's exactly the whole problem. I'm going to fix that."

He didn't wish me luck, but that didn't offend me. I was so certain I was following my divine purpose that I felt I'd make it with no luck at all.

My boss wasn't the only one who reacted that way. When we told any pro-work pundit our intentions, they told us we were crazy for believing we could shirk work.

You've got to be careful with ideas like these, about Sanity and Optimism and Idle Theory. If you go around telling everyone that you're on a search for idle time, for Sanity, you'll be deemed a danger to Mr. and Mrs. American Public.

Because you're Optimistic that the world is abundant and will provide, even without steady work, you'll be called Insane.

I don't know what's to blame, education or civilization or nature itself, but somewhere along the way, everyone became a Pessimist. And Pessimists are, more often than not, work addicts, just like I used to be.

It seems like modern society's soaking in a slimy work-obsessed pool of labor with Pessimism, and if you're not wallowing in scarcity along with them, you're the Insane one. Try to make sense of that logic. Good luck. You might be stuck on that one till the next great revolution.

Anyway, J.R. quit the job he didn't hate but that was partial to Insanity all the same. That was a little tougher, and we both wondered if it was a reckless decision. But that thought only lasted a moment before we persisted with what we knew we had to do.

We got out of the lease on our studio apartment. We went downtown and gave away most of what we owned. Our possessions weren't worth much. Still, it was strange to watch all those things we'd once called ours go off happily with someone else.

We loaded what was left into Sunshine's drawers. We'd owned the bus for upwards of five years by that time, and we had this idea we could do everything we wanted to do, and carry everything we wanted to carry, and go everywhere we wanted to go in this eighty-square-foot space.

Now, I need to cut in and say that you don't need to travel to be a seeker, or to search for Sanity. There are seekers who live in houses and tents and all kinds of other stationary spots. We didn't know it at the time, but we've since met dozens of stationary seekers. Road life was the best solution we thought up to the problem of Insanity, but, really, there are a million gorgeous ways to seek and live and love.

Anyway we took off. I'd never felt more American than that first day cruising Highway One along the California coast, windows down and a big gaping hole of uncertainty before me.

Something happened that day on the road. It seems fantastical, and I'm not sure you'll believe it, but I really feel like you'd want to know. We were somewhere in Big Sur, staring at the elephant seals and considering our new way of life. We were vulnerable without our former securities. We were exposed and bare before the Pacific Ocean. I was scared. We nursed those new thoughts, cradling our newfound emptiness.

The waves crashed and the seals huddled together near the cliffs. Suddenly, a third figure rolled over in the vinyl seat behind us. She introduced herself as

Freedom.

Well, we were pretty shook up about that. I'm sure you'd understand. We'd been driving this bus around for five-plus years, we'd camped in it more times than we could count, we'd driven it cross-country—in fact, we'd driven it every day for 1,825 days—and we'd never seen that rainbow figure inside, not even once.

"That's because I was never invited," Freedom told us. "I would've come sooner, but you were too concerned with comfort."

Turns out, Freedom is the ability to accept insecurity. She's not a bronze statue of eagles and she's certainly not a paper plate of barbecue. No, what I'd assumed was Freedom was actually Capitalism in disguise. It was a convincing costume. Fooled me.

How could we have known? How could we have met Freedom until we stood before the Pacific Ocean with nothing to lose? By shedding our security, we'd inadvertently sent Freedom an invite, and there she was, posing for J.R.'s pictures in the sunset.

We were happy for Freedom's company, but told her what we were really searching for was Sanity.

"Oh, kids, that's a lot to bite off. I don't know if I've met even one person who's seen a glimpse of Sanity from afar. You should be happy for my company. Don't you know that some people spend their whole lives trying to find me? And here I am, moving into your bus."

Speaking from today, I couldn't imagine life without the constant company of Freedom. She continually guides us to the wildest places left in North America. She consoles us when we don't know where our next paycheck will come from. She reminds us of the delicate nature of our own mortality.

Sometimes, she drives the bus while J.R. and I dangle from the windows, singing the anthem of Freedom. That's my favorite.

I'm not always comfortable, but I'm always ripe with anticipation. I'll keep riding with Freedom on my side 'till the day I die and they stick me underground to commune with the worms.

Oh, and that anthem of Freedom? If you don't know her song, here's my advice:

Head out in a direction with no idea where you'll go. Make no plans, set no goals. And listen, because the music only plays, softly, as soon as you've let go of all perceived security.   ◊

GREAT
possibilities
often
APPEAR
impossible

THE GREAT MACGUFFIN

The first time we met the Great MacGuffin was by complete and utter accident. Car accident, that is. I'm not complaining, actually, because if not for that odd bumper bender, there would be no story to tell, because there would be no Tangerine Hot Springs.

It was a day whose sunlight looked like glee, me at the wheel as usual and J.R. to my right. We squiggled down a lone loopy thoroughfare, splashing jokes across the center console and feeling so young you would think we popped out of the comfortable womb of the universe that very morning.

I guided us around a blind curve at a steady twenty miles an hour, and wouldn't you know, we smashed into another orange bus of the exact make, model, and year of Sunshine, her doppelganger you might say, an orange 1976 air-cooled VW.

Now, I insist the collision wasn't my fault because the bus was parked right smack in the middle of the road, directly around a hairpin turn. I guess I can understand how something like that could happen, because the universe runs on a clock of entropy and there's nothing we can do to stop its hands from spinning round.

Aside from our smashed bumper, the collision was tragically silly, two bright orange vehicles kissing in the middle of the road.

"Shit!" I drew to a dead stop and we bounded to the other orange bus to ensure it was unharmed. I didn't see any dents, but then again, these buses are always so beat up it's hard to notice a little extra damage at the end of the day.

The other orange bus sagged under its burden of solar panels, an impressive array of models and designs installed to its sides. There must've been twenty boards of solar silicon squares attached to that camper, draped from every side and glued to every available surface.

Inside the bus sat an old man, microwaving a vegan hot dog and stroking his long white beard. To my surprise, he didn't say a word about our collision. Instead, he treated us as old friends. That was unusual to me, because living on the road, an old friend was one you made six hours ago, and we'd just met the man.

"Good day, glad you arrived in a timely fashion," said the stranger, pressing the microwave's thirty-second cycle.

Just like us, the old man resided in his orange bus. I knew because he had a sticker on his cooler that said "Home is Where You Park It." That really made me happy, because he too, was seeking an alternative to the work-obsessed society that banished bums like him—and now, us—from their safe and tidy living quarters.

The mysterious man remained inside the dark chamber of his home on wheels. Between his beard and his sagacious use of words, he appeared to be an angelic wizard.

"Hello," I greeted him. "I'm Kit, and this is my trusty sidekick J.R."

"I am the Great MacGuffin," he answered.

"I sure am sorry we crashed into you like that," I said.

"Why are you parked in the road around a blind curve?" asked J.R.

"Gotta meet people somehow," the Great MacGuffin answered.

My eyes finally adjusted to the dark interior where the man sat. He sure carried a lot of machines with him in his bus. There must've been over a hundred electronic gizmos blinking and beeping on his counters, in his drawers, on his bed. I wondered where the man slept, but then again maybe someone like that didn't need sleep. Surrounded by his copious collection of electronic equipment, I was certain that the old man was not only a wizard, but—

"Hey, are you by chance a bionic wizard?" I asked.

"I am MacGuffin," said he. "I am the third coming of Jesus Christ."

My eyeballs dropped right into my pockets from pure disbelief.

"Wow," I said. "A robotic messiah."

"Who was the second coming?" asked J.R.

"You should really demand a hundred-thousandth reprinting of the New Testament." I said. "The modern world would welcome a robotic Messiah such as yourself."

But the Great MacGuffin didn't answer. He only retrieved his hot dog.

"I see you've come seeking your quest," MacGuffin said to us, transferring a generous portion of mustard from jar to plate.

"Um," I said.

J.R.'s silence was louder than any protest of agonized boredom in the history of dull conversation.

"You arrived on a fortuitous day," said MacGuffin. "I am interpreting very well this morning indeed. It would be my pleasure to deliver your earthly mission."

He bit into his hot dog and closed his eyes. Apparently, his hot dog spoke to him. He chewed quietly for a full two minutes, humming in absolute absorption as we waited for the message from behind his closed eyelids.

"You two emit a presence like orange eyes in the backseat of a car," he finally said.

"Is that a good thing?" I asked.

But MacGuffin's eyes were still closed.

"It is clear to me that your mission here on Earth is to visit Tangerine Hot Springs," he said.

"What is Tangerine Hot Springs?" I asked.

"It is a place where flowers crowns are all around and hot water gurgles out of the ground. Where Uncle Sam's a nudist and even Christians are Buddhists. It's the place where America washes herself new every morning. Tangerine Hot Springs is every bum's dreamland. On the shores of its holy water is the promise of leisure and idleness in abundance, and very little commitment on the work front." He winked at us. "I know all about your Idle Theory."

The Great MacGuffin continued. "The real draw of Tangerine Hot Springs is that Sanity lives there, for those who care, which I'm assuming you two do. She harbors bums like ourselves from the awful disease of work."

"Sanity?" I asked. "Are you serious?"

"We find ourselves in grave circumstances, seekers," said MacGuffin. "Sanity is only known by a few individuals, and she grows more elusive by the day."

"Yes, I know," I said, hope and optimism slicing open all my restraint. I grabbed MacGuffin by his shoulders. "So know her? You've met Sanity?"

"Yes, of course. I've known Sanity since my earliest bumming days, though we've grown apart a bit. Sanity doesn't keep contact with those who depart."

"Why did you ever leave a place like that?" I asked.

"I am a missionary, spreading the news of Sanity to other bums. I want to share this message with all the seekers I meet. At Tangerine Hot Springs, we bums can shirk work once and for all. We can allow the machines to do their bit and pursue the gorgeous things that make us feel alive."

"But, Great MacGuffin—how will we find Tangerine Hot Springs?" I hoped I could bear the weight of our new duty.

"I have something for you," answered the Great MacGuffin, turning to rummage through a cabinet.

From the tobacco-stained depths of an antique cigar box, the holy wizard procured a small stone of polished petrified wood, encircled with embossed copper plating. The stone was eight shades of orange and glowed with the geologic secrets of its mineralized past. Before the stone's current fossilized state, centuries back, it was an ancient sequoia in present-day Arizona. That's what America told me, anyway.

After polishing the amulet with his sleeve, MacGuffin presented it to me. I thought my eyeballs would surely roll out into my pockets all over again, but they stayed put that time.

"Use this to find your way to Tangerine Hot Springs," said the Great MacGuffin. "You will notice a faint glow when you're nearing the spring."

He gently pressed the amulet into my hand.

The Great MacGuffin then pulled out a diminutive banjo handmade out of cherry wood by Thomas Jefferson in 1773, before the United States of America was known in her present state.

"I composed a song in honor of Tangerine Hot Springs and all the seekers who seek her," said the Great MacGuffin. "This one goes out to the most American place there is."

He belted out his ballad with flourishing vocals, a simple folk song that described Tangerine Hot Springs in language that managed to be at the same time

elegant and heartwarming. The performance culminated with MacGuffin whistling and nearly smashing his banjo in two.

I clapped and bravoed, astonished at the incredible fortune bestowed upon us. So many tramps wander their whole hobo lives with no purpose, and there, on the most ordinary of days, our mission had been appointed to us.

By the look on his face, J.R. was probably pondering his intentions for the upcoming lunch hour. Now, how could he think of food at time like that?

MacGuffin secured his banjo in its case and loaded a pile of dirty towels into a miniature washing machine, the tiniest one I had ever seen. A bionic Messiah indeed, powered by the sun.

"Now be on your way!" he said. "Tangerine Hot Springs awaits, pilgrims."

I thanked the Great MacGuffin for his guidance. As symbol of gratitude, J.R. offered him a photo of our bus, Sunshine, and his orange bus, Tangerine, printed on instant film.

Armed with our new mission, we embarked on our journey to Tangerine Hot Springs, my new amulet safe in my clasped hand and the Ballad of Tangerine Hot Springs in my sparkling pilgrim heart.

"Marching on our pilgrim feet, always headed west," I began.

"—A thoroughfare of freedom beat across the wilderness!" J.R. finished. He grinned and bit into a plum.

We drove off down the road, singing The Ballad of Tangerine Hot Springs, which went a little like this, if you'd like to know: ◊

Ballad of Tangerine Hot Springs

TANGERINE SPRINGS IS FOR OUTSIDER KINGS
IT'S THE REINFORCED SEEM IN EVERY HOBO'S DREAM
A SOAK A DAY KEEPS THE LAW AT BAY
DUNK IN THE STREAM AND FIND YOURSELF REDEEMED

AT THE WATERS OF TANGERINE HOT SPRINGS

FROM CHERRY TREES TO PURPLE BIRDIES
TURQUOISE WATERS THAT COULDN'T GET HOTTER
AMERICA BATHES WITH THE LOWLY AND DEPRAVED
SANITY'S THERE FOR THOSE WHO ARE CARE

AT THE WATERS OF TANGERINE HOT SPRINGS

SEARCHERS ARE SEEKERS AND SINNERS ARE PREACHERS
UNCLE SAM'S A NUDIST AND CHRISTIANS ARE BUDDHISTS
THE COPS ARE HEADS AND DECENCY IS DEAD
PRAISE OR BLASPHEME, THE OPTIMIST'S SUPREME

AT THE WATERS OF TANGERINE HOT SPRINGS

THAT'S WHAT'S SOUGHT AT THE SPRINGS SO HOT
THAT'S WHAT OCCURS IN THE THERMAL SULFURS
THAT'S WHAT'S SEEN IN THE SPRINGS OF TANGERINE
THAT'S WHAT AWAITS THE PILGRIMS AT HER GATES
A PLACE FOR TRAMPS LIKE US WITH AN ORANGE BUS
GO ALONG YOU TWO, JOURNEY ANEW

LIVE LIKE KINGS AT TANGERINE HOT SPRINGS!

Home Sweet Highway

J.R. shoved an atlas in front of my bleary eyes.

"This is it, Kit." His finger jabbed at a point on the map. "See that road? It'll go somewhere we wanna be."

I wasn't even out of bed, but J.R. was on his third cup of coffee. He almost knocked over the entire stove with his searing hot excitement. What I love about J.R. is that he's unsure of his destination, but sure of his destiny. That's a rare trait, so when you find someone who possesses it, you've gotta keep them around.

"I promise, Kit," J.R. said, placing his hand on the atlas like a Bible. "This one'll take us somewhere worth the gas."

We didn't have anything else to do and the day was young, so I clambered out of bed and straight into the driver's seat. J.R. assumed his usual position on the royal vinyl of the passenger's throne, right knee bent and a bare foot up on the glove box. He bobbed his head and ate leftover boiled peanuts for breakfast. They were spicy and his eyes watered and he grinned at the burn. I followed his directions to a small intersection and swung a left. J.R. made a satisfied sound deep in his throat.

"See, Kit, baby, this is a sweet road. A fucking nowhere road. Feel how we slide along? Slick as melted butter over hotcakes."

He curved his hands over the air as though it were thick as matter, stirring the melted butter of the golden light. He looked so serious I laughed a deep belly laugh. Nothing was serious. You could tell that by the way the road wound around the cinnamon trees like a ribbon of butterscotch. Oh beautiful for halcyon skies, was it an orange morning. Sunshine glowed tangerine, like cloudy dreams in the morning sky.

In the world of modern transients, there's a saying. Orange Is Optimism. It's the color of hope. If you see an orange strand of yarn hanging from a hickory tree, it means you should be able to sleep under that tree with little worry of being run off. If there's an orange sticky note on the corkboard of a local grocery store, it means you can call that person's phone number for help, should you need it. That's why Sunshine being orange holds a certain significance to us. She carries all our hope in the future as she carries us across the U.S.

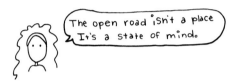

The open road isn't a place. It's a state of mind.

J.R. and I, we want to caress and kiss and savor all the pretty places there are. Black Hills, Great Basin, Snake River, Columbia Falls. These places flit through my head like Technicolor cartoons. I breathe and crave and ache for the pretty landscapes of America. I want to consume them like sugary sap. I want to assimilate every corner of America into my body, so I may belong.

Driving that morning, I was certain I could rush down that exact stretch of road for all of eternity, the wind in my hair, the old ancient fabric of Freedom stitched into my skin. The sky glowed orange and I lost myself in the speed, shedding my questions in the wind through the window. The Where and What of going didn't matter to me at all. It was the Why that mattered, only the Why, and the Why was that it felt damn good.   ◊

Prey for Bears

We hiked fifty-five miles into the wilderness carrying two backpacks and two brains full of information. A low cloud cover obscured the tops of the trees. Two miles down the trail, those heavy clouds opened up and soaked us straight through. We couldn't complain, because in their pressurized intensity, the raindrops cleared our brains of almost a quarter of their information.

The trail was empty, because Mr. and Mrs. American Public don't really like hiking in the rain. It was nice, because they didn't scare away the animals with the perfume they like to wear. A skunk nosed his way through the brambles. A group of Stellar's jays scolded us from their pine tree fortresses. Deer grazed in the green meadows, picking through a salad bar of dandelions and plantain. We pulled strands of spicy green onions from the wet soil and tucked them into the pockets of our backpacks for the night's dinner. We picked raspberries and thimbleberries as we walked up the trail, our fingers nimble in the thorny bushes.

J.R. and I didn't speak once that day. Sometimes we designate conscious days of silence, days in which we don't say a word. It's only healthy to periodically cleanse yourself of your acquired information, to allow it to seep out into the ground to be eaten by strands of fungi.

Around a bend in the trail, I found myself gazing into the molten core of two volcano eyes. A grizzly with a nutmeg coat stood directly in our path, so close I could smell her fur. I froze, wordlessly realizing the weight of our relationship, two apex predators, recognizing each other for the beasts we were.

I became a void, no breath in my lungs, no air in my throat, just the sway of some pine boughs above and her noisy sniffs.

The grizzly stood up on her haunches, tall as a tree. She drew our scent into her nostrils, trying to figure out what sort of creature wandering those green woods smelled like nylon straps. I drilled my legs into the ground like fence posts, bracing for the worst. It was huckleberry country, and I noticed a tremble in the thick bushes. Out walked a fuzzy cub, smelling like a cinnamon stick on an old fur coat.

"We mean no harm to you or your cub," I told the mother grizzly.

Her face was lined with curious doubt.

"I don't deal in symbols," she answered.

She remained on her hind legs, her sniffs desperate, her thoughts no more than an ellipsis suspended over her head. I watched a group of flies on her face. They flitted from her eyes to her nose to her open mouth. I desperately tried to read the language of her body, but I couldn't tell if she planned to charge our way. Then I noticed a slack in her shoulder muscles and I got the feeling she was standing there only to prove a point.

There was a thud as she dropped down on all fours. Having decided we posed no threat, she turned and her cub turned and they ambled away into the huckleberries, just like that.

J.R. and I stood white and stationary as Greek statues for a half hour. We didn't trust that the grizzly and her cub had truly gone. When our legs trembled from shock, and we could no longer stand, we sat and waited, holding eye contact as though the connection of our irises was capable of knitting a force field around us. Neither of us said a word. When it seemed that sufficient time had passed over us, we cautiously tiptoed down the trail, keeping a keen eye peeled for the grizzly.

We hiked the rest of the day without eating, fueled by the sugar of our condensed adrenaline. The blood coursed through my narrow veins. It continued even after we pitched our tent and lay down to sleep on the pine needle ground of the dark woods. All information fled my head, driven out by my pounding heart and bundle of nerves.

The most important thing you can do to heal your civilized wounds is go outside, because in the wild lands, you remember that we are not alone. In our sheltered lives, we've forgotten that we're prey as much as we're predator. We've lost a lot of dignity in doing so, because unless we are willing to lose something, we can never truly enjoy it. This is as true for love as it is for our own lives. We're meant to live with pounding hearts, unsure of what will happen from one deep breath to another. We were born wild and free, and should do everything in our power to protect that wildness.   ◊

we are entwined in a web of miraculous events

call that web reality & it's gorgeous

ALL HAIL MOTHER DUMPSTER

Behind every grocery store in America sits a holy Dumpster. It may not mean much to you, but to a bum, she's a most benevolent deity. Mother Dumpster brims with enough food to feed every bum who has enough sense to glean the glut. Modern people love to throw away food. Not their unfinished hamburger or the last bite of their mediocre fruit salad, but thousands of dollars of perfectly good groceries.

You see, agricultural production is currently at an all-time high. Huge factory farms employ machines and cheap fertilizers to grow cheap corn. Heaps of it. More than we could ever use. And, you know, all that corn has to be made into *something*.

So they form the corn into bars and flakes and box it or bag it and call it Progress. If a box or can is dented, if a bag is ripped or if there's any minor blemish in the produce, the store employees throw Progress straight into the Dumpster. Doesn't matter that the food is still perfectly good or preserved—into the trash it goes. It's an art form this mad world of ours is perfecting: how to throw away more food with every passing year.

Benson's Grocery on the corner of First and Main Street was sure to harbor free food for the hungry tramp. Small and rural, with no modern compactor, it was perfect for us. I'd seen its Dumpster from the road, wide open and welcome.

We swung behind the brown building, me keeping a sharp eye as lookout, peering up and down Main Street at the passing traffic. It was a cold day, under forty degrees. The best possible weather for scavenging. Keeps the food cold, so you don't have to worry about rot or mold or pink bugs that like to eat plastic. I don't know where bugs that eat plastic come from, but I see them in Dumpsters from sea to shining sea.

Don't get me wrong, I'm all for pink bugs eating away the plastic plague of modern convenience culture. My only complaint is that those pink bugs make it difficult for us to eat the food *inside* said plastic packaging. Those pink insects don't like to give up their plastic to humans, no sir, not even if you try to convince them that you just want the food inside. They have no trust, and I guess I can't blame them for that.

Within the cool walls of Mother Dumpster, J.R. dug out three plastic packages of strawberries with no pink bugs on them at all. The entire history of strawberries was transcribed on the packaging like World Civilizations Part I in a pulp magazine.

According to the package, the strawberries were grown in Chile, shipped to the States, and, after a good long shelf life of five days, ultimately put to rest in back of Benson's Market, amidst all the other cheap foodstuffs of modern America. I placed the strawberries in a shipping crate on the floor of the bus and gave thanks to Mother Dumpster.

"Oh, that's nothing," she answered, much too humble for her own good. "It's due to cold weather, I suppose."

"Mother Dumpster, I wish you realized how much the bums of America adore you. We worship your very name, because without you, we'd be working for a living."

Mother Dumpster blushed and looked down on us like a holy Madonna dressed up for the eleven o'clock Easter service.

"All hail Mother Dumpster!" I bowed before the cold green walls of my life force.

J.R. resurfaced with day-old donuts enclosed in a layer of Saran Wrap. What a miracle of the twenty-first century. You can't Saran-Wrap your way to Freedom, but you can further preserve your glazed doughnuts. Once more, J.R. ducked out of sight and came up with strawberry milk, single servings of oatmeal, and three TV dinners, still frozen in their boxes. I ran the food from the Dumpster to the floor of Sunshine, enjoying my work.

Suddenly, a sickening sound pinged through the air. It was like a BB pellet ricocheting off your sister's glass eye, like a sign hanging above the Dumpster reading "No Trespassing, You Bums."

The door to Benson's swung wide open. A bored employee sauntered out, dressed in a red apron and black slacks and lugging a trash bag. His headphones blared hip-hop music. I relaxed a bit. It was a kid. He'd understand.

If you plan to commit any completely harmless but still offensive crime, like trafficking edible trash, you better be committed enough to devise an effective game plan for potentially incriminating moments such as this.

Back in our early days of Dumpstering, we decided it would be best to take a nonchalant approach in the presence of grocery store employees. It seemed the most polite and dignified way for all involved, because it required embracing our actions unabashedly, instead of unscrupulously hiding our true motives. Truth doesn't really exist, but I still honor its memory, for the sake of the great thinkers and religions and gods who have come and gone before us.

So J.R. and I continued as though we were, you know, shopping for a week's worth of groceries. Which we were. We waved to the employee. I said hello. J.R. casually handed me a dented box of Toasted Ricies. I took it to hand and transported it to our bounty of edibles on Sunshine's floor. The kid stood a foot from the Dumpster, considering his next move. Our little game plan was working.

"Uh. You need to move. Get out of the way or get dumped on."

He took a step closer and poised himself to throw.

I understood the decoy strategy, and it was time to lay it on thick as the garbage goo at the bottom of Mother Dumpster. I motioned to our neat pile of food.

"Hey, what about we split this bounty?" I asked the kid. "You look like someone who would enjoy the finer delicacies of the frozen dinner. Come on, let's conspire."

"No thanks."

"But don't you think it's crazy that they throw away all this food?"

"My job is to throw the food away. If there was no throwing away food, there'd be no job for me."

"What if you didn't have a job?" I asked. "Maybe you'd have time to do other things you love."

"I like the money," he said.

"But money is time. Time is money. If you're spending your time on something, you can't merely *like* it. You must use words like enamored. Smitten. Aching."

The kid backed up, like I'd steal his trash bag or something.

"Look. I understand. I think I know where you're coming from." I leaned in close. "Do you ever sit on the floor of your studio apartment, complaining about your studio apartment?"

He looked down, guilty as black sin.

I saw it then. He was a Pessimist, poor guy. Another soul ruled by Insanity.

"Look, I'm no bum. I work for what's mine." His gaze was hard, his jaw set.

"Isn't it true," I asked him, "that you live off the excess of Dumpster culture just as much as us? You need this trash just as much as we do, to make your money."

The kid looked from me to J.R. like we were talking raccoons. Then the Pessimist tossed the huge bag of trash into the Dumpster. It caught on the edge and tore open like a busted heart losing love on a cold winter's night. Its soggy contents splashed all over the food, all over J.R., all over the wall behind the Dumpster.

"Freaks!" said the kid. Then he walked back into the market.

"Hey, well, what do you think Ben Franklin and Teddy Roosevelt were, huh? Choose a side, man! Optimists or Pessimists! Work addicts or seekers of Sanity!"

We resumed foraging, but the remaining food was buried deep under the spilled trash, victims of the Benson's trash bag bombing. It was futile to try to salvage anything.

Just as we decided to give up and move on, what did we see across the street but a creeping cop car banging a u-ey, sly and slick and after us trashy bums.

"Shit! That kid musta ratted us out!"

J.R. jumped out of the Dumpster, outlaw energy hot on his side. We swung out of the damp alleyway, J.R. reeking of Dumpster juice, both of us panicked and wild-eyed and me revving our air-cooled engine in hopes it could sweep us out of the whole bad situation.

Mother Dumpster laughed at us till she hiccupped.

"Go, quick," she said. "Enjoy your strawberries from Chile."

As we sped through the front parking lot, hightailing it outta there before the cop made it to our side, a woman in an Oldsmobile flagged us down. She leaned out her window and handed J.R. a twenty-dollar bill.

"Kids, I saw what happened behind the store. I wish you luck. God bless you. Life is hard. It'll get better."

We tried to refuse the money, but she insisted we take it. She said she knew what it was like to be on a search for something larger than yourself. She thought we'd find it. She told us to find our destiny.   ◊

It all seems
so simple
sometimes.
There's a sky
overhead
& solid ground
to walk on,
Music in the
waves
& clean air
to breathe.

Merry Christmas from Uncle Sam

We couldn't drive Sunshine for a while last year. Don't get me wrong, she was running perfectly. The engine purred, the timing was flawless, and the transmission ticked good as new.

The problem wasn't a matter of physical mechanics. No, what kept us off the road was a philosophical dilemma posed by the government, of all things.

The issue became apparent on a warm day last fall. We were rightly appreciating a fine stretch of freeway when a cop pulled us over. He told us we didn't have a plate or paper bearing an identification number by which he could track our bus. He was polite about it, but sometimes manners are the most depressing thing in the world. The whistled consonants through his teeth almost made me cry.

"You know, officer, you're right," I said. "We don't have that paper. But since you asked, this bus is Sunshine. No name tag necessary."

"I'm sorry, kids," said the cop. "But without that number and piece of paper, this bus just doesn't exist to me or to the government."

"But, officer! You can see with your own eyes that this bus exists."

I was shocked. After all, it's not too often you're asked to prove the existence of anything, besides maybe your innocence.

"Yes, well, I see your point. But can I at least see *your* proof of existence?"

I told him I didn't have one. This led to a lengthy scolding and lecture about general road safety.

"I don't understand. How does a piece of paper change my ability to drive?"

The cop folded his arms. "This is how the Department of Transportation conducts business. Our job is to keep the roads safe."

"And free of imaginary beings," muttered J.R.

The cop handed us a ticket and a packet of forms. "Use these to contest for your existence," he said. "And stay off the roads until you have proof."

J.R. and I, we couldn't believe what we'd learned. I never, ever would have guessed there was a governmental branch dedicated to the subject of ontology. Turns out there's two. They call them the Department of Motor Vehicles and the Internal Revenue Service, and as Americans we had to answer to both.

I dutifully filled out the paperwork, suspicious of the questions. Name? Address? Make? Model? Every question seemed unanswerable. How can you write those things down definitively in ink, like you'll be that way forever? It was more exhausting than the time I had to explain the purpose of cities to my five-year-old brother. Leave it to kids. Or the government.

"Where should I write down we live?" I asked J.R. "They need to know, it says."

"You know the drill with this kind of stuff. Just be honest. That always keeps you outta trouble."

So I wrote down Open Road, Anywhere, USA and mailed the form out from the nearest post office. The lady at the counter enclosed it with a special certification and promised that our proof of existence papers would be delivered promptly.

Months passed. No word arrived regarding the form. During that time, I endured a tragic existential crisis. Who was I? What was I doing here? If I didn't exist, did those months even pass? The questions circled round and round, and I couldn't even tell if they were real.

We waited out the winter in the Florida Keys. There, we reluctantly secured a job digging muck out of a drainage ditch for twelve dollars an hour. We lived in an old man's backyard, amongst a tangle of mangroves, and it was there our qualms were put to rest.

It was the day before Christmas, so we had a holiday from work. We were reading and brewing tea in the bus, listening to the Atlantic Ocean gossip about the European Union, when a knock sounded on the side door.

"Hello!" called a gravelly voice. "Hello to the owners of the orange VW!"

Just outside, an old man sat in a motorized wheelchair, expectantly peering into the bus. It took us a moment to realize, but we were looking at Uncle Sam himself, sweat pouring from his forehead and a "WWII Veteran" sticker on his bumper. That wheelchair was unlike anything I'd ever seen: gas powered and industrial. Believe it or not, Uncle Sam rode that motorized wheelchair all the way from D.C.

to Florida just to hand us two driver's licenses and one registration for an antique vehicle.

"I was supposed to be here three months ago," he told us, "but I'm sure you'll understand it takes a long time to drive around America in a motorized wheelchair handing out official documents. Besides, you kids filled these forms out all wrong! What kind of address is…" he squinted at a three-ring binder. "Sunshine Love Bus. The Open Road, Anywhere, USA? Doesn't exist, kids! I wasted months of tax-funded gasoline looking for you!"

"Good thing we did indeed exist," J.R. said.

"Well, that's up for debate, considering you don't have a proper address to your name," replied Uncle Sam. "See, one of the prerequisites to proving your existence is sustaining a verified residence."

I asked Uncle Sam if he believed this bus existed before he saw its proof of existence, but he didn't seem too concerned with metaphysical questions.

"I don't worry myself with thoughts like that," he said.

"Well, if we can't receive official documents, so be it," I told him. "We have no permanent address. I hope we haven't summoned you here under false pretenses."

"She doesn't mean it," J.R. said, elbowing me. "We, well…we live right here. We have a permanent address. The Open Road!"

"Either way, I have some papers for you kids. Hold on a minute and allow me to find them."

Uncle Sam pulled a stack of three-ring binders from his star-spangled briefcase. He flipped through the pages for ages. It took so long that J.R. got bored and went swimming out to a treasure island and returned with only a rusty pulley from an old sailboat.

Finally, Uncle Sam presented a sheet of paper with my name on it, and then a sheet of paper with J.R.'s name on it.

"You kids better thank the goddess Liberty," said Uncle Sam. "Some careless governmental employee overlooked your problem. Your lack of residence didn't matter one bit. Congratulations, bums. You now exist to me and America and each of our governmental branches, who apparently couldn't care less about accuracy."

I received my papers with trembling hands. There it was, my proof existence, written in clean prose that was easy to read, if you read fourth-century Mandarin.

THOUGHT EXISTENCE WAS SELF-EVIDENT? THINK AGAIN! YOUR STATE OF BEING IS OF GREAT CONCERN TO THE STATE. NOW YOU'RE ELIGIBLE FOR JURY DUTY AND SOCIAL SECURITY. CONGRATULATIONS ON YOUR EXISTENTIAL ACQUISITION. WE'RE SURE THESE LICENSES WILL LOOK BEAUTIFUL ON YOUR BEDSIDE TABLE.

—The Department of Motor Vehicles.

"But we don't have a bedside table," I told Uncle Sam. "Our bed is up in that canvas pop top. It barely fits the two of us."

"Come on, you're tax-paying citizens!" he bellowed. "That camper of yours must have at least a small space for ephemera. A coupon drawer, perhaps?"

"More or less." I visualized the secret compartment that housed our illicit drugs.

Uncle Sam said he really must be on his way, because he needed to deliver an audit notice to a guy up in Maryland. We asked him if he'd finished delivering proof of existence papers in Florida. He answered in the negative.

He told us he abided by an alphabetical system of delivery when serving Mr. and Mrs. American Public, in order to keep everything fair and democratic. He'd be back down in a few months. We told him we'd be gone by then. He asked us for some gas money to get him down the road, because federal funding had been cut, so we donated a twenty-dollar bill and a pan of brownies to eat while he drove. We figured he needed them both, and we sure were grateful to exist.

We added my proof of existence and J.R.'s proof of existence and Sunshine's special automobile proof of existence to a vast collection of documents we've received from the government, like National Park passes and stacks of citations for urban homelessness. Those papers have been lodged there ever since, complaining about Social Security and ranting about dystopian delusions and electoral propaganda.

We evacuated our drugs from that drawer, because they told us all the heavy talk depressed them, especially Pessimistic discourse about the current state of political being. Now, most of the drugs dwell in my clothes compartment. Not the weed, though. Our marijuana's stashed with the kazoos and colored pencils in the drawer above the back seat. It's much happier living there, it says.　　　◊

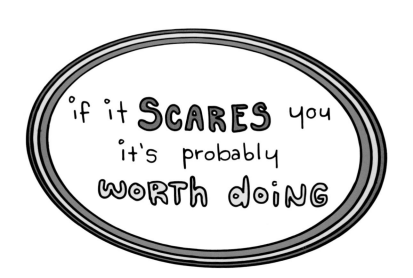

KNEE-DEEP MUD-STUCK BLUES

We crossed the border from Tennessee into Kentucky, visions of wild lost back roads haunting our minds. Perusing the map, we chose a shortcut through the forest and tiptoed in like ladybugs onto a leaf of grass.

I took the right-hander a little too fast, my blood zipping from zero to zillion and back again. We were home, in the green woods where orioles sang from the hillsides and wild turkeys scattered their feathered way through the thick underbrush.

High voltage electricity ran through my body, sending me into such a frenzy that I barely noticed when the road descended a steep hill. First time I realized something might be wrong, J.R. was hooting at me. He made faces like wide eyes with tight lips and squeezed-shut eyes with rectangle lips, and panicked, googly-eyes with white teeth protruding from his mouth.

"Kit! Mayday! Sunshine is spiraling out of control!"

Through the windshield, a tree loomed before us where the road should have been. How the hell'd that happen? I cranked the wheel to the left, and to the left we rumbled for one teasing moment. But then we slid wildly out of control and narrowly avoided a face-first plunge into the depths of a hungry ravine. Sticky mud coated the windshield and I couldn't see a thing, even with the wipers clicked to their highest setting. J.R. stood on the seat, hanging out the window to guide my blind driving.

"To the left! Now to the right!"

I obeyed his shouted instructions. Trouble was, as soon as I steered his desired direction, Sunshine veered the opposite way. It was a regular game of three-player skat, with J.R. and me as the defending team. It looked like we were going to lose.

"Kit! Huge puddle, enormous puddle! Brakes! You won't make it through!"

Oh, I knew better than that. I gunned the gas, smashing the pedal like a can of Coors on a barroom floor.

The speedometer rose to forty miles an hour. My heart sped four times faster.

J.R. ducked inside, his eyes white and wide and his lips drawn tight in a serious straight line. He seized my arm and constricted his muscular fingers till it hurt. "What're you doing?!"

I fashioned my left hand into a hook and squinted one eye shut like a pirate.

"I'm the captain, matey! I'll guide us through!"

"Kit, I'm serious."

"Aw, come on! Nothing's so serious!"

Sudden as a stroke, Sunshine grew wings. One instant, gravity bound us to the earth as it usually did. The next, we soared, flying above that pesky mud puddle in slow motion.

My internal organs left their epidermal prison for a moment. My hair swirled through the air like spores of fungi. I wasn't scared. These are the moments I live for, hot blood coursing through the tubes of my flesh and my mind gliding high above my physical being.

Life isn't meant for comfort. It thrives on these perilous edges, where we just might careen off some cliff to our untimely death. Danger reminds me that I'm alive in the true sense of the word, absolutely combusting.

We landed hard. A rushing sound, like a twenty-foot waterfall, crushed my eardrums. The old stove flew off the counter, all the drawers burst open, cups shattered on the floor, and my collection of books fluttered to the ground like poisoned moths. As a finale, the back door swiveled off its hinge and plopped onto the muddy ground.

Now, silence overtook us, save the rain tapping on the earth and the leaves and a hoarse hissing from the engine.

J.R. wiped his bleeding nose and glared at me. He looked so serious and disheveled, and he cared so much about things such as soaring like a flying squirrel over the puddle. I couldn't help it. Laughter rushed from me in an uncontrollable flood. White-hot anger seethed from each of J.R.'s pores. He lifted his hand as though he would hit me.

"What the hell's wrong with you, anyways? You got a death wish or something?"

He dropped his hand and sighed. A tear of blood bombed his pants crimson as he opened his door with a gory sound.

"Where are you going?" I asked.

"To stomach the damage."

His shoes sucked and popped through the wet clay like clown shoes. I struggled with the door and joined him, buried to my knees in mud. J.R. bent to examine the harm I'd inflicted.

"Dammit, Kit."

His voice took on a serious tinge, like term papers and real jobs and tax season, and I knew something was horribly wrong.

"What?"

"Our drive shaft is completely out. Kaput. No more. We're fucking stuck."

J.R. dug a handkerchief from his pocket and calmly wiped blood from his nose. Then he pitched his bloody hanky straight into the mud.

"Fuck! Why'd you gun it like that? What were you thinking?"

He rattled my shoulders hard. Then, he kicked mud onto my skirt, which was already dirty, but still. That seemed uncalled for. After a moment, probably because I didn't resist, he relinquished me and stalked off down the road.

I put on my best nice-girl smile. "Hey, hey, partner! It'll be okay! We've got water and food and it's so pretty back here anyway. This is home, remember? Just where we wanna be!"

J.R. spun to face me. "You're so selfish, Kit. You always wonder why you don't fit in, claiming you're some kind of victim to be pitied. You know what I think? I think you do whatever the fuck you want and call that Optimism. Then you say it's everyone else's problem that you never stop to consider their feelings. You can call everyone a Pessimist and push them away if you want, but just know that you'll end up alone."

"Stop being such a Pessimist!" I said.

J.R. snorted and climbed in through the gaping black space where Sunshine's

side door used to be. He sure was upset. His nose must've hurt. Best to leave him alone. He'd cool down.

I wandered through the forest, vibrating with the energy of our white hot argument, my brain clanking around my cranium, replaying J.R.'s words through my drum-set head.

His diatribe didn't dampen my spirits, because I'd been called all of that before. Selfish. Delusional. Everyone I knew told me that. That's why I always gave up on them. I knew the truth. I live in a beautiful world. That isn't selfish. That's just smart thinking, considering everyone else endures life as a black and white prison of unbearable boredom.

An acute rumble snatched me from my thoughts, faint but definite and headed towards Sunshine. I raced through the woods, leaping over vines and dodging ferns.

"J.R.! Hear that? Someone's coming!"

"Yeah, yeah. I hear 'em," he said.

J.R. had buried his nasty feelings in the clay. I could tell because he was shooting photos, little dribbles of blood dangling from his nostrils like external organs.

I leaned against the back of Sunshine, staring intently toward the growling sound. Finally, an ATV crested the hill, all muddy and slipping and rampaging. The two guys onboard flailed their arms, braving their wild carnival ride through the woods. I paced the road in the shape of an SOS signal and flagged the guys down. They halted beside us with little snotty grins on their faces.

"Howdy, y'all," said the driver. He was probably thirty, with deeply tanned skin and a black leather jacket.

The guy in back cracked his knuckles, as though the sight of Sunshine in the mud lavished him with bursts of intense pleasure. His shirt was patterned with torn Confederate flags and he nursed a big load of dip in his bottom lip.

"Ouchie! That looks like it hurt."

"Hurt never did anyone any harm," I said. "Good to shake things up every once in awhile. I mean, our wheel peg's all broken, but look at us, doing nothing at all in these beautiful woods. Who could ask for more?"

J.R. snapped a photo of the guys as he approached. "Don't listen to a word she says. We're in the middle of this muck because of her. And it's our drive shaft that's busted, anyways. Wheel peg, my ass. The tires are still holding onto the frame through the torsion bars. Seems like we could roll, but we aren't going to get any power from the transmission."

"Yeah, that's chicks." The driver tapped ashes off his cigarette. "No way in hell I'd ever let my girl drive my truck. That driver's seat, it's sacred space, you know?"

I resented that, but set my pride aside. Those guys didn't know I was the chief driver of the *USS Sunshine*.

"Hey, can you guys tow us out? You think you might have the power?"

"I dunno," said the guy in the Confederate flag shirt. "This thing isn't very well powered and that hippy bus of yours probably weighs in at two tons. Besides, we gotta get back to the compound for the party, don't we, Marshall?"

"What's with all these people coming into the woods on a time frame?"

"Pardon?"

"Never mind." I switched on a voice sweet as your usual fructose fantasy. "Please, guys? It would really mean to the world to me."

"We can give it a try." The driver sighed. "By the way, I'm Marshall." He pointed to his friend. "And that's Babbs."

The guys dismounted their ATV with concrete feet. J.R. rummaged through the engine compartment and returned with a bright red hammock strap. He fastened one end to the ATV and strapped the other to Sunshine's strongest point.

"All right, here goes nothin'!" Marshall revved his engine.

We grunted and shoved. It was tough going. As soon as we made any progress, the mud would take over and Sunshine would slip back downhill. J.R. sacrificed a new hiking boot to the mucky cause. Babbs was strong. Each time he crashed against Sunshine's rusty body, the bus jerked forward like the engine was engaged.

I ran in place, scraping my thighs against the bumper, inconsequential against so many pounds of metal and wood and screws and engine. I sang the first verse of a labor song I knew, an old folk tune, but the ATV engine shut me up quick.

"Kit. And you, Babbs," said J.R. "Let's count it and all push at the same time."

"One, two, three!" We thrust and rammed and hustled. On one unassuming count of three, J.R. pushed at me instead of Sunshine.

"Hey, what's your deal? You really mad?"

As we heaved, J.R. seized the opportunity to kick me in the thigh, so I did the only thing I could. I fisted a clod of mud, spit in it, and shoved it in his face. Before long, we were mired in the throes of an all-out mud brawl, pulling hair and twisting arms and mud caked in our tortured teeth. We were aware of nothing, not even the ticking of dumb time frozen over our angry heads.

That is, until the ATV engine died down and the woods swelled with silence. That's when we realized Marshall and Babbs were slouched against a freed Sunshine, smoking and watching us like a Saturday night special. I, for one, don't enjoy entertaining others. Seems to me like everyone should have imagination enough to entertain themselves.

"What are you two lugnut liberals up to?" Marshall asked.

"Looks like they're grading the road, Marshie," said Babbs.

We broke into unconvincing laughter, pointing to each other and then to the dumb ticking time in the clouds above.

J.R. fought to stand up then, but he soon lost the battle to gravity. I tried my luck next, still half-blinded by the grit in my eyes, and by some sort of fortune I stood. That is, until triumph deserted me and I fell nose-first into a pile of clay. J.R. finally regained his rightful bipedal stance, shaky but sure. I gripped his shirtsleeve and joined him, tottering like a newborn filly.

Babbs and Marshall told us they lived about ten miles away, on a twenty-acre piece of land they called the Compound. Twelve guys homesteaded together, they said, and one of them just so happened to be a junkyard mechanic.

"Slim'll fix you up in under a week," said Marshall. "You guys are welcome to stay on property, if you pitch in with chores. Know how to milk a goat?"

Believe it or not, that little ATV hauled mighty Sunshine the entire length of the muddy double track. Quite the convoy, I'd say. J.R. and I sat in the bus through the curves of Boone county, praying that little hammock strap would continue its show of sturdiness. I tapped my toes against the floorboards. J.R. stared out the window. Fresh blood leaked onto his lips like his mood into the air.

"Hey, you mad at me?" I asked.

"I'm not mad anymore. But I meant what I said."

"Just don't think you're telling me something new." ◊

THERE AREN'T
ENOUGH
MINUTES
IN ALL OF
ETERNITY
TO SEE IT ALL.

Twenty Acres of Anarchy

By the time Marshall and Babbs' ATV towed poor, muddy Sunshine onto their twenty-acre corner of America, the sun was a glimmering ball of red.

"Welcome to the Compound," said Marshall. "The barn to your right doubles as our guest nook and goat milking station. Make yourselves at home, keep all gates closed, and only drink the milk in the pickle jars. Also, no fireworks."

J.R. and I nodded. I, for one, don't enjoy fireworks. They're almost always Capitalism in disguise.

"We're having a party tonight, over by my place." Babbs pointed to a double-wide trailer under an oak tree. "Come on by anytime after dark. Should be a bitchin' time." And they left us alone near the barn.

The Compound was twenty acres of anarchy enclosed by a tall barbed wire fence. Ten double-wide trailers circled the central pond, where ducks and geese paddled amidst an array of multicolored canoes. A lush garden grew near the barn, thick with tomato plants and squash and peppers and rows of herbs that smelled like pizza sauce. Chickens and miniature goats wandered free, picking through tall grass and weeds and a giant mass of junk.

Stuff erupted from every square foot of the property. We couldn't step forward without discovering another treasure, from old washing machines filled with brothel tokens to a signed and framed copy of the Declaration of Independence. There was a pile of tin cans that must've been propagating itself since the American Revolution. We picked through the dried skeleton of a beached whale that turned out to be an old boat frame. In an old delivery truck that said Wonderbread, I found a coffin with Decency lying inside, inert. He must've been sleeping.

Earlier, I'd been so elated to be released from our muddy hell, that it had made me sleepy. Now, my exhaustion was replaced by a searing excitement. I couldn't wait for Babbs' party. You see, it wasn't often J.R. and I came into contact with anyone under the age of fifty. If you looked at our lives from the outside, you'd think Mr. and Mrs. American Public quit procreating in the mid-1970s.

Where are all the young people? We don't see them too often anywhere we hang out these days, not in the woods or the corn belt or the wide-open deserts. I guess most of them are in the city. And I guess they like it that way.

You know the story of rural America. I'm sure they've told you how farming was outsourced to robots. You've heard how factory society then commenced the dubious process of transforming workers into machines. Public opinion concerning rural America went downhill with the advent of the tractor, I suppose. Mass mechanization has been bad publicity for rural living, because lots of urban people think that only robots should do the work of agriculture. That would be fine if it spared us humans some work, but it doesn't. Urban people believe that machines *and* humans should work. It's not their fault for thinking this. It's a simple misunderstanding of work and leisure.

J.R. and I then wandered into a grazzy pasture. There, a tower of old refrigerators rose before us, thirty feet over our heads. It was a playground for the goats, who summited its metallic zenith with glee. A skinny guy wearing a rainbow knit-cap kneeled on a refrigerator eight feet up, where he affectionately blew into a goat's nostrils.

"A girlfriend of mine told me she was creeped out by this heap of refrigerators," he said casually. "So I broke up with her. Nothin' gets between me and my goats."

"What's your name?" I asked him.

"There's a lot of pressure in a name," he answered, stroking a white goat. "That's why I don't go by anything in particular anymore, just something like 'Hey, guy' or 'You there.' On a bad day, said girlfriend called me 'Get out of the house or I'll call the cops, you freak.' That was fine by me. You know, if people call me whatever they want, I'm free to be whatever I want to be. I don't want no fixed identity. No one can limit me to one state of being."

"Besides the government," said J.R.

By that time, it was dark. We followed No Name to the lawn near Babbs' double-wide. Babb's party rocked like the home of the brave. Hundreds of party people crowded around the open lawn, communing with the moonlight. The people wore baggy grunge jeans and afros and long hair and sunglasses at night. A band performed on the bed of a Chevrolet truck, playing machines that looked like neon pulpits. There were four musicians and, somehow, they resembled the faces on Mount Rushmore.

I'd been wondering why it was so warm. Now, I realized the entire night was insulated with goat fur. There were goats everywhere. Grey goats, white goats, spotted goats, goats that spoke Spanish and trimmed their beards for the festivities. I even saw an orange one that looked like Optimism.

They were nibbling on wind chimes and bullying a tiny chihuahua. They were chasing laser pointers across the unmowed grass and bleating as blonde girls in fuzzy pink sweaters cuddled them. I'm telling you, I couldn't look anywhere without seeing a goat. At one point, I thought I saw a hound dog out of the corner of my eye, but I turned to realize it was only a goat in disguise.

Two fridges and a freezer sat like thrones in the cellar, where the Compound members stored the bounty of their land. The first fridge held jars of unpasteurized goat's milk and duck eggs. The second was stocked with Natty Ice and Budweiser. The handwritten signs on the fridge read "Help Yourself" and "Get Less Boring."

Babbs sat on the cellar stairs, conducting an ornate glass bong like a symphony. That bong was quite the piece of artwork, featuring a galactic scene of aliens wearing Confederate flags, shooting each other with bananas. Babbs treated his piece like royalty. He'd light it and contemplate the rig, then signal to his patron the optimal moment of inhalation. "We're going for maximum effect," he said.

One girl cradled a black kid goat as she took a hit. The guy behind her toted a goat with one horn. I wondered if an animal escort was necessary for the transaction, but Babbs told me that wasn't the case, so I shut up and took my turn. As I

inhaled, I saw No Name sitting on the ground near the bonfire, knitting a beanie and talking with a small group of party people.

"Is it true that the guy knitting over there doesn't have a name?" I asked Babbs, staring at his tattoo. It featured a younger, thinner Uncle Sam picking cotton in a Confederate flag kilt.

"Oh yeah," said Babbs. "We call that weirdo Rainbow Boy, but never to his face. He's always claiming he's seen America in some new place, and every time he does, he wants us to call him by a different name. It's kinda annoying, to tell you the truth. But America really likes him, and America brings the party along with her, you know?"

"Yeah, I understand that," I said. "Hey, Babbs. You know Uncle Sam's in a wheelchair now, don't you?"

Babbs took a minute to answer. When he did, a tear glistened in his eye. "No, I didn't," he said. "Thanks for letting me know, asshole." He turned away to service the next jonesing party person with their hit.

I didn't know what upset Babbs so much, but I decided he'd soon get over it. I strolled to the bonfire and sat beside Rainbow Boy. He spoke with the Statue of Liberty's twin and a girl snuggling a fifth of whiskey. The orange goat, Optimism junior, lay in my lap and bleated like a squeaky toy. I stroked his coarse fur, waiting for a lull in the fire party's chitchat. When the conversation paused, because good conversation requires a pause, I tapped Rainbow Boy on the shoulder.

"I was thinking about what you said earlier," I said, "about not being tied down to a name. I've always felt that way, too. I used to think that meant I didn't fit in, but now I realize it means I can fit in anywhere."

Rainbow Boy scratched his back with a knitting needle. He pointed to a shooting star, then gestured an explosion over his chest. "When was the last time you saw America?" he asked me.

"I guess it was just the other day. I saw her in Chattanooga, wiping graffiti off her left cheek."

"She's in the cellar right now," said whiskey girl. "I think she's dealing poker tonight."

"I'll need to go down," I said. "I'm always running into America. I have a question for her, a paramount question, really, but it's so hard to get her to sit down and chat. She's always too busy."

"What do you want to ask America?" Rainbow Boy asked me.

"I need to ask her the directions to Tangerine Hot Springs, where Sanity is found."

"Are you fucking kidding me? Sanity? That's what you're looking for?"

"Yes."

"Damn," said whiskey girl to Rainbow Boy. "She's crazier than you!"

"I don't care if that sounds crazy," I answered, "So what if maybe I am. I'll keep seeking long as I roam this land. It's a dignified quest for a bum seeker like me."

The guy in the liberty crown punched my arm in admiration. "You're like Gandhi with a nicer butt," he said.

"What about a great soul?" I asked, bowing and gesturing like Rainbow Boy had, with the shooting star.

"Whoa, Kit, you need to check out this tree corpse." J.R. called all of the sudden. "No, really, you've gotta see this."

"Excuse me," I told everyone. "I guess I need to check out that tree corpse."

I followed J.R.'s laughing to a glowing orange light in the middle of the thick woods. He was right. The tree was absolutely enchanted. In its lifetime, it must have done some wonderful things, because it was blessed with the postmortem gift of bioluminescence. It emanated all shades of orange light. Best of all, the colors made sounds. We realized after a moment that those noises were the foxfire tree, speaking to us in a strange language we mysteriously understood.

We must've communed with the foxfire tree for dozens of dark hours, asking him questions about regeneration. That night, we experienced true time travel. The foxfire tree told us about Kentucky back in the 1800s. He discussed the evolution of photosynthesis and shared with us what it's like to be consumed by fungi that glow in the dark. After a while, I asked the tree if he'd ever seen Sanity.

"I thought she went the way of crosscut saws. Aren't there chainsaws where you're from?"

I nodded, then fell mute. In the depths of the woods, surrounded by the swirling colors of the foxfire tree, I grew tired and allowed all thought to dissipate from my brain. I completely forgot about America in the cellar, dealing poker. The orange light faded to black, then all was silent.

Next thing I knew, a goat sat on my face as sunlight filtered through Sunshine's drawn curtains. J.R. was snoring with a box of breakfast cereal cradled in his arms, sprawled across the downstairs bed with me. Two strangers were dead asleep upstairs in Sunshine's pop top. I have no idea how they got there, but they looked like gravestones after a hard rain. I decided to leave that scene to fend for itself.

I opened the hatch near the entrance to Babb's trailer and tiptoed down the stairs to the cellar, where a goat was munching Cracker Jack on a beautiful hardwood bar. A group of guys was slumped over it, blanketed by a worn Confederate flag and a pile of old newspapers. A muted television babbled silent news. It was faith through the night, I supposed, to the hungover heroes of the Compound.

It seemed as though America had stepped out only moments before and might return shortly to retrieve her purse. I waited for almost an hour, but she never came back. All I learned that morning was that watching the news is a Pessimist's sport. All the bruises and blood on the screen of that television ate acid holes in my stomach. I didn't know if I'd be able to eat for days.

You won't catch me doing that ever again, no sir. No wonder America didn't come back. I wouldn't either. ◊

Only **optimists** have the guts to follow the pretty **visions** in their minds.

Puzzle Pieces in Paradise

For a while there, I was good friends with Nihilism. We were closest during a two-year period directly after my graduation from university. I was living in my boyfriend's dorm room in Orange County at the time, for the free rent and to buy myself some time because I wasn't ready to grow up. Today, I know I'll never be ready for that formidable task, but that's beside the point.

That year wasn't so bad. My boyfriend would sneak me food from the cafeteria and let me borrow his car. Sometimes he got mad when I invited Nihilism over, but that was only because he didn't understand our relationship.

Nihilism and I liked the same coffee and books and, of course, the Theater of the Absurd, so how could we resist being friends? I think my boyfriend didn't like that Nihilism kept such close company with Pessimism. But since I was also a Pessimist at the time, we fit together like puzzle pieces in paradise.

Back then, I was sure the world was evil by nature. I firmly believed that matter inevitably spiraled into chaos and that entropy won every time. I wasn't yet aware of my own madness and how it consumed me. Of course, I had no idea that Freedom was real or that one day I'd meet her. I never even held that as a goal.

I *was* aware of the presence of Optimism in the world, but wanted nothing to do with her. I was convinced that Optimism only befriended the gullible and naïve. I knew I was neither of those things, because Pessimism told me so. I was intelligent, and my friendship with Pessimism confirmed that.

That year, living rent-free in the dorm room dungeon, Nihilism and Pessimism teamed up and gave me a crash course in what it meant to be redundant. Knowing how to successfully become redundant is a very good skill to have in the modern machine age, what with robotic outsourcing left and right.

You see, I had no job. I had no ambitions. The act of climbing out of bed was sometimes too much for me. Today, I'm grateful I learned the lesson of redundancy at such a young age, because it's saved me a lot of effort trying to be a valuable member of society.

Most people don't learn how to be redundant until they retire or the kids move out. At that point in their lives, many years have come and gone. Most folks spend those many years trying to attribute meaning and significance to society. Eventually, they think back on those many years with remorse. They wish they hadn't made their lives so complicated trying to avoid being redundant when redundancy was inevitable all along.

I will always be grateful for my friendship with Nihilism for sparing me that dark fate. I've forgiven him for some of his darker attributes, like that time he made it impossible for me to get out of bed for two months, because he taught me that invaluable lesson that still guides my life to this very day.

After that rent-free year, I moved to Los Angeles and worked at a crepe stand on the Santa Monica Pier. Pessimism was still a good friend of mine. Nihilism too. We'd sit on the pier and watch all the happy people walk by, eating cotton candy with Optimism. We'd make fun of those people, wondering how they fooled themselves into seeing good in such a depraved and sinister world.

I would roller-skate up and down the Venice Beach boardwalk in my bikini, waving to the boys over at the skate park. They would elbow each other as I skated past, and sometimes that made me happy. I drank leftover wine until 3 a.m. I wrote bad poetry and cursed myself for it.

Jim Morrison lived down the street from me that year on the Venice Beach boardwalk. He told me that sometimes Pessimism hinders creativity. He told me my poetry probably wasn't as bad as I made it out to be. Jim was friends with Optimism. I didn't really understand how someone so intelligent could keep up a relationship like that, but I admired his work, so I didn't think too badly of him. He always saw the sunshiney side of life, and you know what? Sometimes I secretly envied that about him.

It wasn't until I moved into Sunshine with J.R. that visits from Pessimism grew tiresome. We drifted further and further apart, and soon he stopped coming around to people-watch with me altogether. I was so distracted by my newly acquired friendship with Freedom and by finding little hints of America everywhere

that I didn't notice. I just figured he was busy.

Thinking back on it, I was aware that Freedom didn't get along with Pessimism. She was surprised we enjoyed each other's company, because Pessimism didn't think much of accepting insecurity.

I told Freedom that even though so much had changed, my taste in coffee and books was the same. Also, my affinity for the Theater of the Absurd had only increased, so my friendship with Pessimism still made perfect sense.

America hung out with Pessimism from time to time, but wouldn't pay too much attention to his stories about Nihilism. America seemed to enjoy Nihilism's company in moderation, but then, America accepts everyone, no matter their philosophy or faith, so that made sense. I've never met a soul America couldn't get along with.

One day, some time into our wanderings, J.R. asked me if I'd heard from Pessimism in a while.

"No, now that you mention it, I haven't," I told him. "Wonder where he's been?"

We were idling in a field of wildflowers, weaving daisy crowns. Our original intent for the day had been to reach Colorado, but when we saw this field of flowers, we had to stop. We watched the bees and the butterflies float through the breeze. We lay flat and marveled at the migration of clouds across the sky.

I was so lost in the clouds and the curvature of my brain, that at first I didn't notice a loud sort of clanking near Sunshine. But when the sound repeated itself a bit louder, I sat up in the daisies.

On Sunshine's passenger side, near the back tire, a slight figure was whacking a willow bough on the engine.

Now, I didn't know what to do but scream. I had never seen such a curious being, and besides, this creature was sabotaging Sunshine.

J.R. jumped straight up at my scream and caught glimpse of that strange figure ominously whacking Sunshine. Together, we crept to the bus, panting, and peeked into the back. In my clothes compartment, under the back seat, a pair of orange eyes glowed at us.

"Who are you and what were you doing in our engine compartment?" J.R. demanded.

The eyes blinked. "I wasn't inflicting any harm. I just know that every ten thousand miles or so, you've gotta bang on the solenoid to loosen it a little bit."

Turned out, the owner of the orange eyes was Optimism herself. We were shocked to learn she'd been living in Sunshine for well over a year. You see, I didn't know it then, but Optimism is hope that sees potential in the impossible. Which, when we really looked at it, was the foundation of this journey of ours. You see, J.R. and I had started to believe that the pretty visions in our heads would transform into reality. That belief was an honest call for Optimism, and upon hearing it, she'd run right over.

"So you're the reason Pessimism stopped visiting," I said.

"You know," said Optimism, "I've been wanting to tell you this for a long time. I, too, am a big fan of the Theater of the Absurd. It doesn't bother me one bit that Nonsense prevails. In fact, it gives me hope. Maybe it's only because of Nonsense that we can achieve the impossible."

We shared a lengthy discussion about some our favorites plays, like *Waiting for Godot*. It was quite the enjoyable conversation, and Optimism made me laugh in a way Pessimism never could.

Turns out Optimism is just as intelligent as Pessimism. Maybe more so, because she doesn't waste her time talking about scarcity in a time of abundance. Optimism likes small spaces and doesn't require much to be happy, which is why she lived with us so long without our noticing. She spends most of her time in my clothes compartment, or snuggled up in our side drawers.

Just after she moved in, I asked Optimism if she'd ever met Sanity.

"Oh no," she said. "Sanity's elusive as they come. Last I heard, she was out at sea, searching for the long-lost pieces of herself."

"Sounds like us," I mused.

"It certainly does." ◊

WHEN YOU
BECOME ON
THE OUTSIDE
THE WAY YOU
SEE YOURSELF
INSIDE
YOU ARE
TRULY FREE

STAR DUST RAG IN C

In the Grand Escalante, I learned how loud a coyote's wail can be. It was a night so dark the black of it rang through the air like the Liberty Bell. A nighthawk hunted mosquitoes and bats crisscrossed the crisp night like zippers in the sky. J.R. and I spread our sleeping bags flat on Sunshine's roof. We lay still and reverent, unlike the sky. The sky couldn't keep itself together. Dozens of shooting stars dashed across the Milky Way in a silly race to annihilation.

At first, we assumed we'd caught a random rush of shooting stars, but they multiplied until we lost track of how many there were. That's when we knew we bore witness to a special event. It was a Wowie Meteor Shower up here on Wowie Mesa, and we were just in time for the show. A particularly large shooting star burned out in the center of Cygnus, and I turned to J.R.

"Are you afraid of dying?" I asked.

"Of course," he answered. "Aren't you?"

"No, not today," I said. "Today I feel as though I've lived a whole lifetime, in the best and biggest and realest of ways. Tonight I will sleep happy, because I knew today."

J.R. shifted his weight and clicked his tongue. I could hear him smiling through the silence.

"Damn, but it's good to be alive," he said at last.

That's when the coyotes appeared across the landscape, crawling boulders under the starlight. A dozen of them circled the bus, their eyes glowing like yellow stars fallen onto the ground. Their screams shot through the night, mimicking the sound of debris flying through space.

They yipped and yowled at the meteor shower, rife with irrepressible life, fully aware that we wide-eyed humans were sprawled on top of the bus. Judging by those wild howls, I believe they enjoyed a good bit of fun at our reaction.

A rancher we met once told us that coyotes can smell gunpowder. He said he'd never seen a hint of a coyote while riding his pastures with his shotgun. At times we entertain the idea of traveling armed, but that night I was thankful we didn't carry anything besides the rusty Red Rider BB gun we found in a barn back in Omaha. I wouldn't have scared this moment away for anything in the whole universe.

You know what I think? I think the coyotes gathered to tell us they knew we were searching for something they'd found. Maybe it was something they'd never lost in the first place. It could have been Sanity. It could have been the way to Sanity. It could have been any number of things, and I sure would've traded most anything, even my dignity, to hear their secret. Only it wasn't time for us to know yet. There was nothing to do but keep listening until we knew.

After a while, the coyotes slunk away, their eyes mischievous and yellow as they crept through the sage and slipped into a thicket of pinion and juniper trees. J.R. and I climbed down from the roof. Inside, we fell into a strange sleep, one haunted by glowing eyes and inescapable annihilation, our vacuous longing spread thin through the brittle stardust night.   ◊

FREEDOM FROM WANT

Have you ever waded knee-deep in Dumpster goo? I wouldn't recommend it. But, I guess I do a lot of things I wouldn't recommend you do, so that's not saying much.

Anyways, that was us, J.R. and I, spelunkers in the cavernous innards of Mother Dumpster, knee-deep in Dumpster goo, when suddenly a street bum appeared around the back of the alley.

Street bums usually lead a coarser life than nomadic bums like us. However, judging by all the things he carried, this fellow in particular was enjoying a streak of luck.

He was pushing a shopping cart that overflowed with brand-new stuff, a portable television still in its box, a down coat shielded from the elements by Saran Wrap, and a cell phone case displaying a genuine crystal money sign. It absolutely reeked of Capitalism.

"Where did you get all that new stuff?" I asked him.

"They were handing it out near the Freedom from Want Party office the other day," he answered.

"Who?" asked J.R.

"The Freedom from Want Party. You know, that organization founded by FDR and immortalized by Norman Rockwell? They're always giving away free shit."

"Why do they do that?" I asked.

"Shit, I don't know," said the street bum. "You don't ask questions when unsolicited charity offers you the extravagant surplus of Insanity."

"Did you have to show a proof of existence to get all that?" I asked.

"Fuck no! I don't exist to those people. That's exactly why they give me stuff. If I went around validating my existence all the time, I don't know what would become of me. I guess I'd have to get a job."

The street bum parked his cart beside the benevolent bosom of Mother Dumpster.

"Hey, if you kids want to hand me the food, I'll make a pile for me and a pile for you."

"Sure." It was only fair, seeing as this Dumpster was his turf and all.

But as we dredged the depths of Mother Dumpster, all we found beside bags of paper towels was a lone platter of sushi.

Mother Dumpster apologized for the lack of food. "I really do feel bad about it," she said.

"It's okay, Mother Dumpster," we replied. "We know you always offer your best to us."

We three kings of vagrancy sat at the saintly feet of Mother Dumpster, enjoying our snack.

"You kids'll want to check out the rally in town today," said the street bum. "It's held by the Freedom from Want Party. They give away the tastiest meatball sandwiches. The party is languishing so much in this part of the country, they let you take as many as you want. They're even hot!"

"You'd think if they were languishing, they'd quit giving away sandwiches. That's insane!"

"Well, you know what they say about Insanity," said the bum.

"What's that?" asked J.R.

"She's the creator of bums! The holy creator of Mother Dumpster!"

"No shit," said J.R.

We finished the lone roll of sushi and bid farewell to the street bum. Then we strolled downtown, where we could scrounge ourselves a real meal.

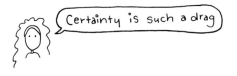

Freedom refused to join us at the FFW's downtown office. She wouldn't be caught dead at a political rally.

"I don't care how good the sandwiches are," she said. "And besides, I should sue for misrepresentation of my name."

It had been a long time since I'd had a good meatball sub, and J.R. hadn't eaten since last Tuesday, other than the sushi, so we showed up at the FFW office at precisely noon. The rally turned out to be a lot like a Fourth of July celebration. There were tons of cheap novelty items, including eagle-printed paper plates and frosted cupcakes and—yes—even sparklers. Capitalism was there, wearing his Freedom costume, but he didn't fool me for even one minute.

J.R. and I approached a card table where fruit punch was being poured into tiny Styrofoam cups like the blood of America onto a slaughterhouse floor. A man stood near the fruit punch stand, wearing an air of authority and also the most gorgeous mahogany leather dress shoes I'd ever seen, polished up like a wood floor. If I owned a pair of shoes that fine, I'd want to be named after them. I decided to bestow upon the man the same honor I'd want and call him Mr. Mahogany.

"Excuse me," I asked Mr. Mahogany. "Do you know where the meatball sandwiches are?"

He looked at me first, and then at J.R., who clutched a red, white, and blue cupcake in each fist like double torches of Liberty.

"The sandwiches won't arrive until two or so," he said. "That's when the needy are to form an efficient line to the left of town hall, in order to receive their lunches. I assume you passionate young members of the FFW are in attendance to put your political fires to good use?"

"I think my political fire would be put to its best use burning down political platforms," I said.

His eyebrows shot to his hair line and he shot me a rocket's red glare.

"Well, that is witty, young lady," said Mr. Mahogany. "Perhaps I'll employ your services in the FFW donation booth today. I'm assuming you're familiar with the expression 'Vote with Your Dollars'?"

"Is that the slogan for that store at the corner?" asked J.R. "The one with the yellow dollar sign and enormous empty parking lot?"

"I thought that place was called Dollar Delite," I said.

The man laughed. "Haha! We have before us two comedians, Elva!"

Elva didn't look up from the red, white, and blue sign she was painting.

"Well, let's put 'em to work," she said. "Give 'em a microphone. No better way to gain members than to distract them with mindless humor."

I got the funny feeling that these folks *knew* this party was celebrating Capitalism in disguise. I wondered if they hadn't stitched together Capitalism's costume with their own sewing machine.

"All right," said Mr. Mahogany. "Since you two are the youngest members of the Freedom from Want Party in attendance, why don't we assign you our most glamorous positions? How do you feel about leading the parade?"

"How about leading the sandwich line?" asked J.R.

Mr. Mahogany presented a false donkey head.

"One of you will march as our beloved mascot, Freedom Fred. The other will pilot the parade and its participants holding this banner." The sign read "Hegemony is No Enemy."

Just as we were truly plunging into all-out panic, someone pulled Mr. Mahogany aside.

J.R. grabbed my sleeve. "Kit," he said, "do you think this is really worth a meatball sub?"

"I was just thinking the same thing. Maybe we should—"

But it was too late. Mr. Mahogany herded a middle-aged crowd of political pundits into the party's office. They smelled vaguely of disappointment and fake strawberries.

"All right, everybody!" said Mr. Mahogany. "I hearby call this rally to order. I would like to present to you the bright young members of the FFW who will conduct our march today. Come on up you two!"

With legs of dreadful lead, J.R. and I dragged ourselves to the podium where Mr. Mahogany stood.

"Hello," I greeted the crowd when we arrived. "J.R. and I are only here for the meatball subs!"

The crowd laughed.

"Great sense of humor, these two," Mr. Mahogany told the crowd. "Now, let's go out there and free the needy from their wants!"

J.R. wielded the sign, because it was over three feet tall, and as much as I hate to admit it, he's stronger than me. I dutifully donned the donkey costume, because it happened to be just my size.

That afternoon, J.R. and I were on our best behavior. Once I forgot it was a rally for the FFW, I actually kind of enjoyed myself. There was music, including

one especially catchy pop tune called "Free from Want Is Truly Free." America was there, eating cupcakes and banging on a drum. This was just her kind of scene. I saw a guy riding a float who looked just like Uncle Sam, but he disappeared before I could speak with him.

I didn't even bother keeping an eye out for Sanity. I knew she wouldn't be caught dead there, because everything about the FFW rally was the work of Insanity.

We marched through the streets singing "America the Beautiful." America blushed and said we were being much too kind, but I knew she secretly adored that sort of attention.

I learned a lot about politics that day, like when everyone sang the last line of that song they loved, "From sea to Chinese sea." It freaked me out at first.

But, after I considered the ambience, with all the talk about voting with your dollars, and Capitalism in disguise, it made perfect sense to pay tribute to our overseas partner in Capitalism.

The other line they sang "Crown thy brothers with useless goods" really summed up the sentiment of all the plastic Lady Liberty costumes.

I was glad when, at the end of the day, the parade fizzled out and Mr. Mahogany arrived to collect the Freedom Fred donkey outfit.

"You two did a truly marvelous job today," he said. "Perhaps you'd be interested in taking a position with the party. What do you two do for a living?"

"We are willfully unemployed," J.R. answered.

"You are too much!" Mr Mahogany said, loud laughter escaping his lips.

"Well," I clarified, "specifically, we're currently employed in searching for Tangerine Hot Springs, a place of Sanity."

Mr. Mahogany cracked up. I wasn't sure why he laughed at everything we said, but I supposed it was preferable to the alternative.

"I was wondering," said Mr. Mahogany, "if would you two would be interested in attending a private social function tonight? Since you mentioned it, the event will be held at a thermal spring, and is open by invitation only. And, well, I am extending my invitation to you."

"A hot spring?" The volume of my voice rose beyond the limits of my control. "You have access to a hot spring?"

"Shh!" Mr. Mahogany's eyes burned like coals behind his glasses. "This is a private affair, and if you cannot conduct yourself with appropriate decorum, I will have to withdraw my offer."

"No!" I held up my hands. "Please. It was—"

"Don't listen to her," J.R. said. "She has a thing for sulfur."

Mr. Mahogany peered at him.

J.R. shrugged "People are into stranger things, man."

Mr. Mahogany regained his rigid posture. "Very well. You two wait here. I'll retrieve my vehicle and return shortly. We must depart immediately if we're to make it in a timely fashion."

"Well, that was a bust," said J.R. as Mr. Mahogany walked away.

"Why?" I asked, my mind fixated on this newly promised hot spring.

"Kit, we didn't even get a meatball sandwich."   ◊

HALLELUJAH I'M A BUM

The FFW's event was no more than cocktail party, something I usually despised because I'm not one for inane banter.

This, however, wasn't your usual cocktail party. It had two things going for it, both of which assured me there would be no inane banter that evening. First, everyone there was naked. Second, it was held in one of the most gorgeous stretches of national forest I'd ever seen, the name of which I must keep a secret, to retain its dignity. I hope you'll understand.

The hot spring itself was nestled into a pristine alpine meadow. Orange lanterns shone between two stands of aspens, illuminating an elegant creek that tiptoed through the charcoal forest. The stars flickered like tea candles above, and nude bodies milled throughout the dandelions, sipping from champagne flutes and discussing what I thought must be the most important ideas in the world.

I was only mildly surprised to discover that the FFW was a society of nudists. You never know what sorts of unacceptable hobbies people practice in private places, cut off from the general public. People talk about truth like it's real, but I'm telling you, they are never honest about what actually matters to them.

I had a good feeling about this place, what with the nudity and general feeling of dignity in the air. J.R. did too. He beamed through the dark and swung his camera to his glowing face.

"Absolutely not, young man," said Mr. Mahogany. "Photography is strictly forbidden at our private hot spring. Please, disarm and conceal your camera or you will be escorted from the premises."

J.R. deflated, but cooperated.

"Very well, then," said Mr. Mahogany "Let's change. I will meet you in the bathing area."

I mussed my hair in the changing room mirror, slouching over, furrowing my brow, doing anything at all to make myself less attractive. If you want to be taken seriously, you must detract from youth and beauty as much as possible. Sometimes it seems like if you want to be regarded as a serious thinker, you're required to either live a long time or get it all out and die young.

The only decorations in the changing room were endless lists of rules. They stretched on and on, each rule punctuated by an etched dragonfly. Made me feel like I was in a city. No unshowered bodies. No excessive sweating. No photography. No overt self-promotion. No guests without prior permission. No fascists. No off-hours visitation. No offensive language. No controversial subjects. No dyed pubic hair (it stains the spring).

Then I noticed a curious small door near the locker room, and I couldn't help but peer inside. In a romantically lit room sat a robot that vaguely resembled Mae West. Her lips were rouged in fabulously and her fingernails were slender and elegant.

"That must be the most beautiful machine I've ever seen!" I told a woman nearby, who turned out to be Elva from the Freedom from Want parade, wearing bright pink lipstick and taking off her robe.

"It's an E-Lover," she said. "Everyone's been lusting after these for a while now. No fights, no misunderstandings, no compromise, always ready."

"Wow," I said. "And I was impressed to meet a robotic Messiah!"

She gestured to a second door. "There's a male counterpart, if you're interested. Looks just like Clint Eastwood. He's a hunk."

I hadn't asked how the loving was executed, but then, I didn't need to. An unclothed man entered the room and began doing things with the Mae West robot I'd never seen someone do with a machine before. I shut the door before the relationship progressed too deeply.

Surely these were the chicest people I'd ever met. Remarkable, like a new race of humans, completely entwined with technology. I've had many relationships with machines, but I can't say I've ever enjoyed one so intimate as the one that man grunted into behind the little door.

I emerged, nude, from the dressing area, the moonlight glowing with old wisdom on my skin. I fingered my woven hemp necklace with its petrified wood amulet to remind myself of the lofty goal assigned to us by the Great MacGuffin. I hoped this was it. Tangerine Hot Spring.

I accepted a champagne flute from a server and held it as gracefully as I could as I walked over to the hors d'oeuvre table. It made me smile to see America and Thorstein Veblen over by the bar, taking hits off an old soapstone pipe. Freedom had refused to join us and Optimism was too shy to even ask, so it was just the two of us at the nudist hot spring, me grinning under the moon and J.R. blissfully holding a plate of fancy appetizers.

"This makes up for the sandwich, huh?" I asked him. J.R. grinned, all bits of food between his teeth.

Mr. Mahogany approached us at the table, freed of his clothing and looking more relaxed than we'd seen him all day.

"Why don't you two follow me to the spring? There are some powerful folks representing the Freedom from Want Party over there. They'll be tickled to meet some youngsters on fire for the cause."

I felt guilty about deceiving Mr. Mahogany, even though in reality, he'd chosen to fool himself. We'd told him we weren't interested in politics, but just like most people, he didn't believe the honest truth when it was presented plainly before him.

Mr. Mahogany led us to a group of six standing under another illuminated list of rules. As we approached, I felt all twelve eyeballs run over my body.

"Nice to see young people with minds wide open here at our little gathering," said Elva. Her pubic hair was shaved into a heart, something that almost made me fall in love with her.

"My mother always told me not to open my mind so wide everything would fall out," I said. Elva giggled. Mr. Mahogany cleared his throat.

"Everyone, I would like to introduce to you Kit and J.R. These two are bright young members of the Freedom from Want Party who assisted Elva and myself at the rally today. I believe that hardworking folks like these are our hope for the

future. In a bleak world, it's good to see young people shining for Freedom."

A man with a peace sign tattooed on his upper thigh introduced himself as Gerry. Largely unimpressed by our arrival, he returned to his cell phone after we said hello. The presence of his phone set off a ripple effect around the party, like talk of bombs on national television. I had no idea where they had been before, seeing as there were no pockets at a party like this, but still, every phone within one hundred yards of Gerry bloomed in the night, lighting the woods with a cosmic blue glow of connectivity.

I devised a quick plan to distract the FFW members from their cell phone obsession. After all, it isn't often J.R. and I share conversation with people of society.

"We aren't really much for politics," I told everyone. "We're pilgrims, on a quest for a holy hot spring. See, this search is both spiritual and physical, and it was appointed to us by our wise guru, MacGuffin. He's a robotic Messiah."

I thought that last part might impress them, mechanized people that they were, but everyone was completely absorbed in their cell phones.

"Why don't we enjoy a soak?" Mr. Mahogany suddenly pointed to the steaming spring beside him. "After all, isn't that what we're here for?"

That hot spring was blistering as a Fourth of July picnic in Winnemucca, and the water must've been six feet deep. The women clutched the side of the pool to keep their heads and glasses above the water line.

"The water's a hundred and eight degrees," said Elva.

"Sizzling," said J.R., who looked like a frog boiling for supper.

"Elva," said Mr. Mahogony, "I have a suggestion. Perhaps you'd like to share with our guests your new venture. I'm sure they would be delighted by it."

She nodded. "I'm much obliged to. As you probably know, modern America is afflicted with an insatiable want for material possessions. And as the Freedom from Want Party, it is our duty to free the public from their wants. The problem is that we have been overly successful in our efforts.

"There is an excess of material goods being distributed to the needy. We have raised the luxury level of the handouts to the point that bums are littering our streets with their unwanted cheap stuff and demanding extravagances such as tickets to the opera and cruise ship vacations. That is the first problem.

"The second problem is slightly more complex. You two probably don't know this, but bums pick refuse from Dumpsters to fulfill their material wants."

"We've seen the inside of a few Dumpsters in our day," J.R. said.

"Well, um. Good. Glad to hear it. You'll surely understand our problem here, then. The issue is that the Freedom from Want Party is in direct competition with Dumpster culture. We conducted a few studies this year and found that bums prefer the anonymity of Dumpster diving over our perfectly good handouts. It was quite a surprising discovery. Can you believe that bums will salvage food and other items from Dumpsters before they will ever consider coming to us? Apparently they consider Dumpsters a more dignified source for procuring their wants."

"Yes!" I agreed. "Mother Dumpster is a saint and a queen!"

"This lady knows her stuff," J.R. said to me.

Elva paused, looking concerned. She took a sip of champagne and continued. "To resolve the problem, we commissioned a local robotics engineer to design a cost-effective trash compactor to be supplied to every retailer, including grocery and clothing stores. That way, bums can no longer Dumpster dive and our partners in manufacturing can continue to spin the cycle of goods that keeps the Freedom from Want Party afloat."

"Wouldn't it be easier to tell bums to be happy with what they have?" I asked.

"You can't tell people to be happy with what they have," Elva said. "The economy would absolutely fall apart."

"The economy is a new science," I said. "and sciences aren't to be trusted entirely, because they exist indoors, in artificial realities, where life is not."

"Why not just use what's already in the Dumpster?" J.R. asked

"I don't believe you understand what Elva is saying," said Mr. Mahogany. I could tell he was trying hard to be patient. "By eliminating Dumpster diving, we create more want. That is the premise for our new project, the manufacture of subliminal want. If we are successful, the Freedom from Want Party will maintain our control over subsidies to the homeless. We need to act, and act now! If we don't get this issue under control, we'll lose our jobs to those filthy Dumpsters!"

J.R. spoke up. "As a bum, I myself suggest that you allow everyone to salvage their own goods from the Dumpster," he said.

A stern voice cut in from above. "Manufacturing handouts for the homeless contributes to Progress. And Progress comes before rationality. Everyone knows this!"

I'd recognize that face anywhere. It was Uncle Sam, nude and eating baked brie on that motorized wheelchair of his.

"Progress is the mother of Insanity," I said. "And Insanity builds an ugly world."

"The Progress that you're poo-pooing created you," said Uncle Sam. "Without the economy, you wouldn't exist."

"At least we wouldn't have to prove we exist," retorted J.R.

"Educated young people are excellent at crafting convincing arguments," said Uncle Sam. "Best of all, they're always right!"

Everyone laughed.

"So you say you know Dumpster culture well, do you?" said Elva. "I'll bet neither of you transients contributes to the economy. Do you pay taxes?"

"We work from time to time," J.R. said.

"But only when we have to," I added. "We reserve our right to be lazy."

"These two are bums!" said peace sign groin man Gerry, pointing his finger at us while looking at his phone.

"Why should I get a steady job when you're hogging two for yourself?" I asked.

"I can't believe it," exclaimed Mr. Mahogany. "You are only bums!"

"That's what we've been telling you all along!" said J.R. "Glad that's cleared up."

I stepped in. "We stopped working so much because our modern excess of work destroys beauty. Addiction to work perpetuates the myth that the world is a scarce place. It creates a society of bleak Pessimists!"

"The Freedom from Want Party is not concerned with Optimism," said Mr. Mahogany. "Only fools believe that the world is generous. It is a scarce place, and we must work to build abundance! Optimism spreads romantic myths that must be dispelled. She is a propagandist for what's sane, and everyone knows that Sanity destroys civilization!"

"Well," I said, "Optimism lives in our bus and I can tell you this: she is helping us search for Sanity, because we want to live in a beautiful world of leisure."

Everyone exchanged glances, then resorted back to fiddling with their phones.

"Hey," I said loudly, "don't you think it's rude to sit there on the phone while someone is so passionately pouring their heart out to you?"

The only sound was Uncle Sam biting into a crostini.

J.R. laughed, as though to say, "You've really done it now, Kit."

I could smell Mr. Mahogany's anger like the smoke of a thousand fires.

"Has it occurred to either of you degenerates that perhaps we have business to attend to on our phones?" he demanded.

"No," I said, "it hasn't. Because this is a party, not a business meeting. I pity each one of you, afflicted as you are with a bad case of the old Puritan work ethic. That should have died off as a rare disease years ago."

Suddenly Elva slapped the champagne glass out of my hand. It shattered across the pretty marble edges of the spring. "I believe people should live beautiful lives," she said, "so long as they first mind their manners."

For a moment, the party was quiet. Even the crickets singing in the summer's air hushed themselves.

Mr. Mahogany marched straight up to me, halting that painful moment of silence. He yanked me out of the hot spring like a rag doll.

"How dare you! Coming onto our turf, parading around as though you believed in the Freedom from Want Party. Why, you're just two privileged white kids glamorizing bum life and poverty instead of joining and perpetuating the systems that profit from it! You are fools for rebuking the FFW. You were born to become a member of the party, to contribute to Progress with hard work. You only attended this meeting to belittle our cause. You blaspheme the very culture that created you."

"All we wanted was a meatball sandwich," said J.R. "And everything turned to Halloween."

"Enough." Mr Mahogany threw his glass on the ground. "Get these bums out of here!"

A burly man seized J.R., while Gerry and Uncle Sam circled us to ensure we wouldn't resist.

At the pretty aspen gate, the men shoved us out with the force of a car wreck. J.R. and I hit the dusty ground with a muffled thud. Our clothes came after us, landing near our faces.

We lay on our backs, staring at the night sky, naked and breathing hard from the struggle. I really should have told Elva something when she slapped that glass from my hand. Manners are a bore to me. They make me feel hollow as a dead tree.

Drops of water clung to me, still warm from the hot spring. The Milky Way tried to sneak across the sky without the moon noticing.

I looked to J.R. "Well, that wasn't it, was it? That was no Tangerine Hot Springs."

"You can rarely tell what anything is by what people say it is," said J.R.   ◊

Why not
wake each bright
new morning
so sizzling
with the fat of life
that you crackle
d burn
& almost explode
with the
big & small things
that make life
miraculous

Selfies are Deadly

Awoman was killed in this parking lot last week. It was a perfect afternoon in the Badlands when the incident occurred, with a dozen or more witnesses present to recount the tale in its entirety. From what the authorities pieced together, here's the report.

Around 3 p.m., a male bison moseyed leisurely between the RV campground and the bustling gift shop. He was keeping to himself, as bison often do. His stroll was interrupted by a woman fiendishly snapping pictures on her iPad.

If you had asked the woman to be honest, she would have told you that taking this photo was the only reason she visited the national park at all. Earlier that morning, she had made a checklist to be sure she'd accomplish everything she wanted while on vacation. If she could only cross off "selfie with bison," she could go to town, hit the coffee shop, and spend the rest of her vacation sending emails to her boss in New York City.

"Hey! You there." The woman held up her left hand, which meant something to her, but very little to the bison. "I need you to slow down for my picture."

"No," said the bison. "I'd prefer not to."

That particular bison was known throughout the national park community as NR #803. He was regular as a stopwatch. All the locals knew his daily commute. Most afternoons, he walked from the gift shop to the parking lot, across the busy road, and into a green meadow to the south. There, he would chew his cud and bathe in the late afternoon sunlight until night fell over the land.

On that particular summer's day, the bison had used up all the patience his bovine body could carry. The tourists were thick as mosquitoes in July, and he simply needed a few moments of peace away from the buzz of the crowd. It was perfectly understandable, his desire to be alone, and most humans respected it.

But a case could also be made for the woman. She herself had endured a frustrating day within the rugged boundaries of the national park. A squirrel stole her son's sandwich, there were no showers in her campground, and it turned out traffic was no better in the park than in Greenwich Village. The annoyance she already harbored from the day bubbled and boiled over at the bison.

"Isn't it your job to pose with visitors? You can't live on publicly owned land with no useful purpose. This isn't a country of freeloaders!"

The woman had read that wildlife photography was the national park's main activity, and she intended to return home with photos for her Facebook page.

"But, of course, I know what's fair," she added. "I'm known to tip generously." She dangled a ten-dollar bill between her manicured fingers.

"My great-grandfather had no use for money and I intend to carry on the tradition," replied the bison.

He looked both ways and prepared to cross the busy intersection. Fast as an antelope, the woman scurried beside his wooly chest and snapped a selfie.

At first, the bison only experienced slight exasperation. It wasn't the first time he'd been disrespected. However, when the woman began altering the selfie with filters and overlaid text, even making a rainbow vomit fall from his open mouth on her Snapchat app, the bison grew irate. Unable to control his anger, he backed up a bit and ran full-speed into the distracted woman, goring her through her torso. She died that evening from the wounds inflicted.

Three days later, the bison was subdued, to use the language of the federal authorities. His behavior branded him a danger to Mr. and Mrs. American Public.

The woman's phone survived the otherwise fatal goring, and the offending selfie therefore remains preserved. They printed the photo on high-quality card stock, and today it's hanging from a wooden sign near Big Fish Creek Pullout:

DO NOT TAKE PHOTOS WITH ANIMALS. SELFIES ARE DEADLY.

I looked at the display for a long time, a true testament to the uncommon nature of common sense. In the photo, the woman looks happy, but she has a double chin. The bison's eyes are closed and he seems about to sneeze. It's one of the worst photos I've ever seen, certainly not a piece of art worthy of double homicide, but then I suppose that all sorts of intelligent people and kindhearted wildlife have died over causes and desires even more trivial than this.   ◊

Optimism is HOPE that sees POTENTIAL in the impossible.

THE NEW AGE GROWS OLD

The day we swept through Jasper, Arkansas, I scheduled an appointment with Dr. Aikan at Karl's Drive-In.

The professor and I were buddies throughout my university days. Specifically, I was Professor Aikan's teaching assistant for a graduate history course. In those days, I thought I wanted to be an intellectual. Back then, I didn't know I had a body. I'd been fooled by years of schooling into believing I was only a mind. You can imagine the relief I experienced at the discovery of my own body. It's spared me hundreds of dull days cooped up in an office.

Professor Aikan waited for me at the Drive-In, grooving to the Moody Blues in his orange Cadillac. I climbed in and joined him on the bench seat. To look at Aikan, his multicolored Hawaiian shirt, sandals, and goofy grin, you'd assume he was die-hard for Jimmy Buffett. I'd say, however, that Aikan was more into Nietzsche than anything else.

Those days, Dr. Aikan was retired, living on a humble piece of land in the Ozarks. I hadn't seen him in years, because he was too busy questioning the nature of reality to be seen and, besides, this was my first time through the Ozarks.

The rock 'n' roll music put me in a good mood, and Professor Aikan sure knew how to make me laugh. The waitress skated out a cheeseburger for him and a hot fudge sundae for me and the mosquitos dined on our flesh in the noontime shade.

Professor Aikan asked how everything was going. I told him it was a classic American story, one he'd read too many times already.

"Perhaps you'd prefer an origin tale," I suggested. "I was born with the innate skill of improvising Canaanite mythology at the drop of a top hat."

"I'll pass on that," said Professor Aikan. "I'd rather hear your own myth. Anything else would be too exhausting. Usually, the stories people tell about their own lives are completely fabricated. That's the sort of thing I like to hear. I'm not one for truth. That's why I studied history."

Despite his astute nature, Professor Aikan never gained esteem in the field of history. I never understood why. As his T.A. for graduate course HIS 509, I contend that the ideas he posed were brilliant. Never mind that they discontinued the course after only one semester. He was one of the only people speaking any sense in the entire university, him and some of the books in the library.

"Art lies enough to be true," Professor Aikan liked to say. "History? It tries much too hard to be truthful and everything winds up sliced into lies."

Half the students dropped the class the very first day. Guess truth is the toughest subject of all, even if it doesn't exist. Personally, I haven't believed in truth in years, and to be honest, it's been such a relief. There are much nobler ideals to defend. Like poetry. And beauty. Once you're worried about truth, poetry and beauty disappear.

Because Dr. Aikan insisted, I began the story of my post-collegiate life.

"A few years back, I realized I was insane and that everyone around me was insane. It seemed crazy to sit around being crazy, so I moved into a VW bus and started searching for Sanity."

"Bravo! That is an all-American story." The professor dipped a french fry into mayonnaise. "It couldn't be more red, white, and blue. The bourgeoisie is convinced that the myth of America is dying, but, young lady, that was excellent. America herself may not be able to orate a more American story."

"Now," I continued, "I'm looking for Tangerine Hot Springs. It's the place where the cops are heads and decency is dead."

Aikan's eyes glazed over in all shades of flashback blues. "That was a much desired destination back in the sixties," he said. "Back then, we called it the New Age. It was a place to discover Freedom."

"Freedom's my roommate," I said. "She's pretty cool, but she's sort of a snorer."

To see Dr. Aikan smile, you'd think I'd told a bad joke.

"At times it seemed we were close to the New Age, but we never quite found her. Sometimes I think she was afraid of the light shows and loud music, so she left. Glad to hear she's still out there, even if she's in the form of a hot spring now."

"You know who's supposed to be at Tangerine Hot Springs? Who I want to find

more than anything, Aikan?"

"Who's that?"

"Sanity. Did you guys ever come across Sanity out there, when you were after the New Age?"

"Sanity, huh? That's a good one." Dr. Aikan laughed until he realized I was being absolutely sincere.

"We had a few bouts with Sanity, back in the sixties, but I can't say I recall any of them clearly. All I can remember is leaving more confused than when I showed up. Kid, you're better off looking for America."

"The Great MacGuffin told us America herself is also known to frequent Tangerine Hot Springs."

I didn't add anything about how much of America I'd seen. Seemed better to keep that to myself, after his reaction to Freedom.

"Is she now? I suppose that's exactly where America would spend her holidays."

Aikan suddenly commenced an excavation of his trouser pockets. He produced a leather-bound copy of the Constitution, a bus ticket, and an old stogie left over from Woodstock. Finally, he removed a brochure whose front cover showcased a black and white photograph of a swimming pool clouded by billowing steam.

"Have you heard of Hot Springs National Park? It is supposed to contain some of the most developed hot springs in the United States. It seems likely to hold your Tangerine Hot Springs."

The book smelled like a dustbowl song in an Oklahoma windstorm and its weathered pages creaked like a rusty crankshaft as I flipped through them.

"Wow, Aikan! You really are a gentleman, and I'll always say that about you."

Our waitress roller-skated to the Cadillac's window and told Aikan that he had a phone call waiting inside. That made me feel like it was 1982, gas prices were at an all-time low, and President Reagan was in the White House.

"I'm sorry to cut our meeting short, but I must go," said Professor Aikan when he returned from his phone call. He slipped a cardigan over his bright orange Hawaiian shirt. "I just received news that a former student was arrested for a misdemeanor involving his multiple identities. You know you are permitted only one identity in the eyes of the government, Kit?"

"Oh yes. I just received my proof of existence."

"That's what the nation's coming to," Aikan sighed. "Anywoo, there's a hefty bail over his head. Figure I'll help the kid out. I've spent a few seasons in jail myself, and this time of year is by far the worst for incarceration. Best leave that till winter."

"Wait." I connected the vague dots scattered like constellations through my brain. "Is it Brett?"

"How did you know?"

"Brett told me years ago that he'd get put away. Damn. Glad to hear that dreams do come true."

Professor Aikan hugged me goodbye. "Tell the New Age hello for me," he said. "I'm not up for the search anymore."

His Cadillac disappeared from the Drive-In like last season's dress shoes. I waded out of the ketchup-stained parking lot, inspired by Brett. If you're convinced something will happen, and desire it with deep passion, it will manifest itself into reality. I suppose that's precisely what Optimists do. We transform the impossible into the possible.

If Brett could obtain his dream of unlawful detainment, why the hell couldn't I discover Sanity out on the beat-up road?   ◊

when I look out my window

I see a beautiful world

Tramp! Tramp! Tramp!

We swung by Hot Springs National Park as Professor Aikan had suggested. At the gate, we flashed our proof of existence papers to the bored ranger, who pointed us in the direction of the springs. We sped toward them, full of hope. The park shone with orange glimmers of promise, at least for a minute it did.

Then, a certain incident occurred that involved me hanging out the window while Freedom drove down the park road at thirty miles an hour. It also involved a post on the internet that the park service saw immediately. Guess they were bored, because they even sent the cops after us. When they pulled us over, I told them there was nothing to worry about.

"I was only chasing the spirit of Sanity with Freedom at the wheel," I said.

"That is all well and good, young lady," said the cop, "but so far this summer, our staff has responded to two vehicle rollovers in the park, both of which resulted in serious injuries. Unfortunately, this type of incident is happening more often as we see increased traffic on our gravel and dirt roads. We do our best to provide safety messages to visitors, but your behavior and Instagram post provides some mixed messaging. Seat belts are legally required by drivers and passengers in the state of Arkansas and it is illegal to ride outside of a moving vehicle."

With that, before we even had a chance to soak in the hot springs, the police escorted us out of the park with a newly acquired ticket and threats of eternal banishment from every national park there was, so you better believe we won't be going back to that zoo any time soon.

Tired of the whole crazy scene, we decided to blow off the Ozarks. We descended their worn green hills and hit the pin-straight farm roads west, whizzing into the plains, past the fields of wheat, corn, and soybeans that make the world go round.

That afternoon, we surveyed the wide expanse of Kansas for the first time. The horizon was a charcoal line, so straight only God could've drawn it. The land's linear lateral movement whirled my mind woozy, and the sky screamed ecstatic prayers that traveled wide without an echo, no walls to hit.

In Kansas City, we swung by the library of the state university. We'd heard on the local anarchist radio station about an author's reading event happening on campus that very night. Normally, we wouldn't much care, but the event advertised free pizza, so you know they were almost begging us to go.

The university library reminded me of a dream I had once, about endless rows of file cabinets falling over into a card catalog eternity. J.R. and I each grabbed a slice of pepperoni as I tried to forget the memory.

The author read from his book, which was about the Work Ethic in Industrial America, of all things. I wish I could say otherwise, but the reading was difficult to sit through. The book was, as you'd have expected, another propaganda packet touting the virtues of work. Disgusting material, really. It took all my energy to refrain myself from interrupting. I kept picturing another slice of everything pizza, and that's the only way I made it through at all. J.R. fell asleep five minutes into the reading, leaving me to endure the dreadful service in that church of work all by myself. The hour crawled by like a day in a factory.

Finally, it ended, and we loaded up on more pizza. We had just stuffed our cheeks full when a student approached us, his arms crossed and brows knitted.

"How did you like it?" he asked.

"It's a lousy argument," I said. "America's drowning in technology and none of those machines have lightened the workload? Isn't that the whole point of Progress, to reduce our collective labor? Why would our workload increase with technological advancement? Sounds like a pile of boloney to me."

"Are you two students here?" he asked, eyeing us up and down.

"No," said J.R. "If we had our choice about things, which we do, we wouldn't be in the university."

"Well, we came to the event tonight," I chimed in. "But we're not enrolled here. We're just curious about the American work ethic."

"And cheese sticks," said J.R.

"Yes, I noticed," the student said. "It seemed you enjoyed the speaker very much. Your snoring spoke volumes."

J.R. beamed in response.

"So," said the kid. "If you aren't students here, what are you?"

"We're seekers on a quest for a holy hot spring," I said. " You see, we were living in the city, working all the time. We realized it was insane to work so hard for things we didn't really want. So we decided to work less and allow machines to replace us."

"How do you make money?"

"Oh." I waved his silly question away. "Money isn't really hard to come by. If you're willing to take whatever job comes around, it all works out."

"We harvest fruit," said J.R. "We've mowed lawns and built some fences. Recently, we helped butcher chickens. Whatever job comes around, we'll take it."

The kid looked at us like we'd stolen his college degree. "Ah," he said. "So you two are migrant laborers."

"I guess so. Also known as hobos. Bums who occasionally work."

"Fascinating," said the kid. "As the child of immigrant migrant laborers, I'm most curious. Has your work with them given you insight into their world?"

"Well, I guess so," I replied. "When you travel, you're given the opportunity to see into many bizarre and beautiful worlds. There are so many gorgeous ways to live, after all."

An ugly smile crossed his lips. "Do you find the migrant laborers to be as spiritually and mindfully aware as you have become?"

"The only thing we're aware of is where the good pizza is," said J.R.

"Do you find it strange that some migrant laborers, like my parents, desire the 'Insanity of modern life,' as you put it? Do you preach to them, coming from the other side, about how destructive modern life is and how you've both escaped it to join them as praiseworthy hobos?"

"No, we mostly talk with them about where to find work or how hot it is in the field. Metaphysics isn't always appropriate. Anyway, I'm no proponent of truth. You can't preach without a truth to tout, can you? It's simple, what we're doing. We're working less, gaining more idle time, and searching for Sanity."

The kid leaned in close to my face. "Your mission stinks of unchecked white privilege," he said.

"What do you mean?" I asked.

"It is disingenuous for you to claim that your income comes from farms. There is no way you do work like that. You are entirely ignorant to the suffering of the migrant worker."

"But most of our income does come from farms," I said to the kid. "Look, I wish we didn't have to work, but it seems necessary sometimes. I'll let you know if I find a way to avoid it completely."

"I guess that's the thing about life, said J.R. "Suffering can never be extinguished."

"This is the downfall of America," said the kid. "The privileged forgoing their privilege and choosing to live like the oppressed. Upward mobility is dying, and along with it is the American character! You can only live with less because of your privilege. You can only enjoy it because of your privilege."

"Maybe all of us would enjoy the privilege to simply be, if only we worked less."

"Thanks to people like you, the oppressed will be forced to accept simple living forever. Think of that as you parade around."

He stalked away, muttering to himself. We watched him approach the author from the church of Insanity and whisper something in his ear. Then he pointed to us. When people point at you after finding out you're a bum, that usually means it's time to leave. J.R. and I located the nearest exit and dashed down the stairs, away from all the potential trouble brewing in the library.

We bolted from the University of Kansas campus and parked near a reservoir.

Still hungry, I cooked up some sausages over the old propane stove. Like hobos back in the roaring days of rail hopping, we built a fire near Sunshine's door. I think often of the hobos and bums who paved the way for us modern nomads. They, too, hid way down a forgotten weed-ridden road, just wanting a quiet place to rest their tousled heads for a night.

I liked to think they'd be proud if they could see us, hidden out of sight, bathing in the still waters of the reservoir, looking into the diamond sky, not worrying about anything further off than dinner.

Our plan was to rest our bodies there by dark and then move on in the morning before dawn trembled with its first rays of light. Don't worry about us, dear reader. We were three counties over before the earliest rising citizen of that small-time Kansas town took their first sip of coffee from their favorite porcelain mug. ◊

TRASH BAG FULL OF FUN

Ihave no idea where they came from, but two rainbow kids walked straight out
of the woods just when it was time for dinner. We were camped ten miles down
a dirt road, in a section of Sanders County that sounded like whistling songbirds.
The boys were about sixteen years old, I guessed, and they wore baggy jeans that
dragged on the ground. They introduced themselves as Pokey and Smith and told
us they were headed four hours east, just the way we were going.

"Could you spare a ride?" they asked.

"I can spare a few erroneous thoughts," I said.

"Can you ever," said J.R.

"Does that mean we can have a ride?" asked Pokey.

"Sure," I said. "Would you like some chili? Mother Dumpster was feeling especially magnanimous today. There must've been twenty cans in that bin."

The evening painted the clouds a pretty pale shade of pink. We stood outside
the bus eating big mouthfuls of hot chili straight out of the pot, a communal
Dumpster feast.

Pokey struggled with a black trash bag that was about to burst. I had no idea
what those guys were lugging around like that, ten miles down a dirt byway, but I
didn't pry. Seemed better to let our relationship progress naturally. I didn't want to
hear some strange story about a corpse.

Smith had with him a traveling companion, a tiny grey kitten that sat on his
shoulder like a parrot. It mewed and blinked its blue eyes and dug its claws into the
boy's skin, grasping its precarious perch with all its might. I thought Smith was so
groovy with that cat on his wide young shoulder. I imagined him to be a villainous
pirate of the open road.

We washed up after dinner, running our fingers through cold water and scraping chunks of chili from our bowls with our fingernails. Then J.R. declared it was time to get moving.

"It's getting dark, after all," he said.

The kids settled onto the floor of Sunshine and initiated the important business of sharing their life story. Every bum, tramp, and hobo knows that out on the road, your life story is the most valuable asset you carry. You see, to tell your story is to prove you exist, and that proof is paramount to the human ego. To ramblers, that proof of existence paper from the government doesn't mean a thing. It's your story that matters, and you better have a good one or else you're a goner.

Smith packed a bowl, working slowly because he had so much to say. Words popped through his rainbow lips like water through a percolator.

"We ran away from home last year," he said. "But we're no bums. We're part of the working class."

Pokey and Smith had just completed a season trimming weed over in California. There, they stored up a hefty stash of the goods to sell back East. That's what Pokey had been struggling with. Pounds and pounds of stinky, delicious marijuana. A trash bag full of fun.

The boys treated that trash bag full of fun nicer than they probably treated their mothers, gingerly positioning it in a safe spot and repeating over and over, whenever one of them moved an inch or I turned Sunshine, "Don't jostle the weed, man. Don't crush the nugs!" The pungent green aroma gave me a secondhand high.

"We're fuckin' set," said Smith. "We traded the other half bag of weed we harvested for food stamps up in Humboldt. You know, you've gotta eat somehow. It got us weeks worth of bacon and strawberry milk. We just sat down by a river enjoying that for a while. We smoked almost a quarter of our earnings, but hey, a celebration was in order.

"No matter what we do, we cannot smoke any more. The rest of this weed must become cash—and quick. We figure it'll get us enough crisp bills to live large the rest of this year."

As they finished their story, the kids dropped small squares of white paper onto their tongues. J.R. and I perked up.

"Hey, guys, you got some extra paper sunshine? We'd sure pay you for some."

"No. We're awful sorry. We'll definitely leave you with some herb, you know, we respect your ride and the dinner. But this is the only acid we've got."

They seemed genuinely apologetic. But they didn't know that I can see colors without sunshine rainbow blotter paper. They didn't know that right then we were a spaceship shattering a glass wall of gravity, neon planets whizzing past so very fast in the dark.

An hour up the road, the kids' eyes were round rainbows staring through the dark. They were seeing all shades of all sorts of colors, just like me, and the sounds of them were grainy and impure and I really liked that about them. J.R. climbed into the back with Pokey and Smith and shot their rainbow eyes with his digital camera, coalescing their energy by capturing it on film. The next morning, he flipped through his photos and was disappointed to find they were only a jumble of vague shadows. Certain experiences simply can't be captured, I guess.

A while back, I had installed a whiteboard on Sunshine's icebox. Every day I wrote a new thought there, to perpetuate the beautiful ideas I'd like to transform into reality. On that particular day, I scrawled:

AN OPTIMIST IS THE MOST RADICAL THING YOU CAN BE.

What's wrong with quoting yourself, after all? I was proud of that sentiment when I wrote it. But the way the kids with their rainbow eyes repeated it over and over, like an ad for health insurance, made me squirm. For a minute, my defenses bristled in the sacred name of poetry. Some people have no sense of what's sacred. They'll speak any old word the same way they'd summon the name of a holy deity.

But then I remembered their white squares of paper. Despite their irreverence, I liked these kids. They carried an orange aura about them. They had their trash bag full of fun and were certain that was all they'd need to make it good. I understood that feeling. Every bum knows you don't need much to live a good life. We drove along happily, painting every road and overpass orange, all the Optimism in the world piled into this little bus.

"Hey, you guys ever heard of a place where flower crowns are all around and hot water springs straight out of the ground?"

"Oh yeah," said Smith. "The Elders in the Rainbow Gatherings are always talking about that spot."

"Really? What do they say?"

"You know, how great it used to be back in the day. It sounds pretty bitchin' still. Tangerine Hot Springs, I think it's called."

It was strange to hear someone speak this holy name so casually, blasphemy to my devoted ears.

"Don't you understand? It's—"

Our conversation was interrupted by a whining siren. Arresting colors sliced through the night, blue and red, angry eyes of the heroes of America.

"Oh man," I said, steering to the right. "The cops. This is gonna take a minute. And just when the conversation was actually going somewhere."

The kids freaked out at the very mention of the cops. They scurried and skidded and rustled their trash bag full of fun against the floor.

"Don't jostle the *weed*, man. Don't crush the *nugs*."

"Never fear!" I told them, rolling down the window. "We know how to enter these situations. Honesty always prevails."

The cop shone his flashlight over my face, over the dash with its sage smudges and handwritten anarchist signs and feathers and paraphernalia, and over my hands, which drummed on the wheel.

"Dudley, state trooper," he asserted.

"Kit, upstanding citizen," I asserted.

"J.R., societal outcast," J.R. asserted.

"Could you watch the light?" I asked him. "It's shining right in my eyes."

He ignored me, then inhaled deeply. I followed his lead. That weed had an aroma like the limestone streets of emerald heaven.

"Do you know, miss, why I pulled you over?"

"No, I don't. In fact, I was just thinking earlier today about the phrase 'Pull over.' What does it mean, anyway? What exactly are we pulling?"

"That's quite enough, young lady. Where are you heading?"

"We're headed west," said J.R. "No roads in America go east."

"Never mind him," I told the cop. "That, that's a good question! I, along with my compadres back there, who are in the midst of seeing rainbows, are on a mystical voyage to a magical hot spring. It's the color of tangerines. You see, we're looking for the place where a soak a day keeps the law at bay."

The kids crackled up a commotion behind me. Their trash bag groaned as though it was being put under.

"I'll need your license and registration," said the cop.

"My proof of existence! Of course!"

I hadn't been asked to prove my existence too often since receiving my official papers. Uncle Sam would be proud. I dug through the glove box and handed my proof of existence and Sunshine's special automobile proof of existence to the cop.

"Doesn't it seem strange?" I asked him, "that something as magical as our existence can be reduced to mere paper?"

"All righty, miss. You wait here while I enter this into the system." He walked back toward the slicing red and blues, talking into his radio. "We've got a case number 636."

That's when the commotion kicked up. Smith and Pokey had been baited with fear, and I heard their feet thrash as they were snared in the deadly trap of paranoia.

"We are in deep shit now, dudes," said Smith, his face nestled between J.R.'s left ear and my cheek. The kitten jumped off his shoulder and onto J.R.

"Deep, deep shit. That number he said? It's code. He's calling for back up. They're gonna search us! We've gotta hide this weed!"

The kids were losing their melting rainbow minds, scooping the weed out of the trash bag and into our drawers, my clothes, those wide pant legs of theirs, anywhere. They were dead straight convinced that the cop was gonna search and probe and rape every square inch of Sunshine, from the cooler and glove box to the trash can and screw holes. The noise of their thrashing was immense.

"Just don't crush the nugs!"

Pokey, who until that moment had remained entirely silent, grabbed his own two chubby, childish cheeks and pulled on them till they seemed ready to abandon their neighborhood between nose and ear.

"My skin is stretchy, dude! I think it's gonna ooze all over our weed."

I grew annoyed with those two rainbow-eyed clowns. Didn't they know that honesty's the best policy? I always say be honest—no one'll believe you anyway. Use that to your advantage. Tell an honest story, because it's the best fiction there is.

"Chill out, you two," I said. "I was completely honest with that cop. He has no reason to search us."

"Are you kidding? Here we are, tripping balls—"

Smith was cut off by Pokey's horrific wails.

"Or at least he's tripping balls. And you're gonna tell the cop about it? Of course he's gonna bust us!"

Poor Pokey placed a pot under his arms to catch his dripping skin. He sobbed on Smith's shoulder, convinced that he'd not only crushed the nugs, but also contaminated them with his aqueous flesh.

"I'm gonna pay you back, man," he cried.

"Stop it with the epidermal meltdown already." Smith shoved him away.

J.R. tossed Pokey a bandana. "Would you mind cleaning up your mess, please? I try to keep a tidy house."

Pokey calmed and obediently wiped Sunshine's wood floor. He really put some effort into it, and our floor was soon cleaner than it had been in months.

"Two birds," said J.R.

That's when the cop returned, clutching my proof of existence.

"All right, miss, I'll tell you what. I looked at your record, which is clean."

"Yes," I agreed. "I told you the whole truth and nothing like the truth, which is my duty."

"Just listen." His voice sagged, raspy and wilted. It must've been the end of his shift. "You, girly, and your boyfriends back there."

A shriek from the back. Pokey's wail could cut through quartz.

The cop continued. "Your brake light is out. Here in Sanders County, we consider that a grave offense. It is an incredibly dangerous stunt that is absolutely forbidden within my jurisdiction."

Suddenly, an owl hooted his low notes in the sky.

"Hey, officer, I know this is incredibly important, but do you by chance hear that owl calling back there?"

The cop handed me a small, translucent piece of paper. I received it like a treasure. It was bright orange and that really made me quite excited.

"Hey, due to this orange color, have you by chance heard of a place called—"

"Lady, you are making me tired. Retain that ticket and fix your brake light. If it's not repaired in ten business days, you will receive a mighty large fine. Continue on and never let me see you in my county ever again. Do you understand?"

"Officer," I said, "before you go, I would like to make you an offer you just can't refuse. The two young men seated behind me are bright young entrepreneurs, and for one day only, they're offering the finest selection of emerald heaven you can find anywhere in, er, Sanders County. One of our young professionals is tragically enduring a grave medical issue and they have established the good business to raise funds for his treatment."

Pokey poked his head into the front. "I'm a human puddle, man."

"Would you quit it with all the nonsense? Get out of here, you kids, before I change my mind."

The cop walked off, shaking his hands as though they were covered in sticky jam. He must've been going through a rough time. I hoped he'd be okay.

"Look, J.R., he gave me this driving award."

Quiet sounds murmured through the back of Sunshine. I turned around. Smith was rooting through all his hiding spots, retrieving the hidden weed.

"Looks like the nugs got crushed," said J.R. "But, hey, all's well that ends well!"

"You guys are fucking crazy! Keep the extra weed. We're out!"

The side door slid open, and Smith and Pokey sprinted into the black woods, beyond the scope of our headlights. You know, to this day I'm not sure why.   ◊

Take comfort. Our lives aren't as important

as they sometimes seem.

Always Go Swimming

July opened over the land like a wildflower. It was almost America's birthday and everyone wanted to throw her a party, because two hundred and forty years is a long time to us humans and longevity is worshipped as the noblest virtue there is.

There must be millions of parties thrown in America's honor every year, and what amazes me most is that America shows up to every single one. That's the best part of the holiday, even though I'm not really a fan of birthdays.

My least favorite part of the Fourth of July is that everyone says that Freedom is at their party, even when she's not. It makes me feel like I'm crazy, because I can see flags and signs and cupcakes saccharine with frosting and even sparklers, but in ninety percent of those cases, Freedom isn't there at all.

You'll be in a campground on the Fourth of July and over at the next campsite they'll be talking to Freedom, flattering her as though she's standing beside the river, telling her that her earrings look so stylish in the late afternoon sunlight. But Freedom isn't there. I know it because Freedom doesn't have pierced ears. I know *that* because she's always losing her clip-ons in my clothing compartment.

The partygoers never have any clue who's *really* at their party, and that's Capitalism in disguise. Now, I told you before that I was fooled by Capitalism's costume most of my life, so I guess I can't blame people for misunderstanding, even though it drives me crazy.

That particular July, in Teton County, we were invited to one of the parties held in America's honor. It was at a rodeo arena. Trailers and campers circled on the dusty ground like those were the early days of America and we were pioneers, safe in our wagon encampment on the plains. It was a regular summer party, you know the kind, hamburgers with ketchup, watermelon, talk of fishing, children losing fingers to sparklers and M80s, and in the distance, calves bellyaching about their lot in life. Like true summer, there was a feeling in the air, warm, like eternal youth.

A Boy Scout troop pitched their tents near Sunshine and immediately erected the largest American flag I'd ever seen. That entire troop could have shared it as a blanket, but I don't think they'd ever do that.

That evening, they conducted a ceremony for retired American flags. The scouts stood at attention as their leader sang the National Anthem through a karaoke system. Big tears of pride and honor cascaded down the man's face as he sang. One of the mothers in the back was eating a cupcake and the noise of the tin wrapper assaulted the anthem like a foreign invasion.

"Land of the free," the scout leader sang, "and home of the New Age."

No one laughed besides me and America, who was over by the dessert table, eyeing the fireworks. I knew she'd heard the line because she spit out her beer like a Roman Candle. That got me going. Then there was J.R. I knew he'd heard it, too, because he held up two red and white plastic whistles like proof through the night that, even if we did laugh, America would always have our backs.

It was tough, because we couldn't really explode with laughter. You know what happens when people think you're mocking their ideals. That's it for you, villain, bum. You're outta there.

We contained ourselves as the ceremony continued. Two boys marched in tandem, hoisting a torch that crackled with flame. They passed it to the scout leader, who offered it to a frayed flag that looked like America's dirty underwear, which I guess it was. Oh say did that star-spangled banner yet blaze. The karaoke machine blared "God Bless America" through the dirt cathedral of the rodeo grounds. The somber crowd stood in rapt attention. One man cried as he watched the flag combust, as though America herself was being cremated before our very eyes.

◊ ◊ ◊ ◊

Wanting to throw our own party for America and Freedom, we ditched the rodeo grounds the next morning. On the crest of Porcupine Ridge, the meadows proudly displayed their yellow bloom of arrowleaf balsam root like offerings to the sun.

We snagged a spot in a thicket of white-barked pines that groaned with its irrevocable beauty, until we walked outside and the mosquitoes descended on us like flesh-eating zombies, which I supposed they were.

The Fourth of July weekend passed us by easier than any flag-burning ceremony, hiding out in our bum's camp on the mountain. We burned big bonfires of downed pine as a family of beavers swam happily by. We read Walt Whitman out loud and made tea from the voluptuously ripe rose hips that grew outside in brambly bushes. J.R. whittled us a new wooden spoon out of a fallen cedar limb. I cooked stew in our cast-iron pot.

On the day of America's actual birthday, we decided to celebrate by going somewhere we'd never been before. We crossed the river that giggled through the woods and climbed something like six miles through the trees, no trail, no map, only our own intuition to guide us. The tense muscles of the thick forest relaxed to a glacial alpine lake that glittered blue against stubborn mounds of marred snow. Dirty as it was, we ate of the leftover snow, hints of last season's winter sweet on our tongues like stolen liquor from my parents' wine cellar

Before I could say a word about it, J.R. dropped his clothes and bolted into the lake, as though it was all so spectacular it just might disappear on the back of a flying dragon.

"Wowie, is this water cold!" he screamed. "Wowie, check out that mountain! You don't have to worry about the skeeters in here, Kit! Wowie, it's so cold I can barely breathe! You need to get your butt in here, Kit, and savor this deep and clear experience of being alive! Like a dream! A verified dream!"

I sprinted to join J.R. in the lake, that special lake whose waters tasted like powdered sugar from the freezer. In those blue waters, we chanted "Wowie, wowie" and sang "Happy birthday, America, whatever party you're at now, and thank you Freedom, good friend, for all you do, and thank you, mosquitoes, for the reminder that you can't enjoy life without a bit of discomfort."

That day, ten thousand feet up in those mountains, we saw God. He was sharing a shell with a small snail. He told us that in the fall, he'd die and come back again, that resurrection is a process that mends together each of nature's four seasons. I didn't understand what the snail god told me at first, but a few hours later it glittered like a disco ball over the snow-peaked mountains.

In those holy waters, I understood. Life's a miracle that lasts only a moment, and because of that, you should always go swimming. Always, always.   ◊

HOBO$

It was August and the worst time of the year to get a job. The sun glazed over the mountains like melted honey, and all we wanted to do was wander the winding alpine trails of northern Colorado.

Only one thing separated us from lazy afternoons at 13,000 feet, and that was money, or rather, lack thereof. We desperately needed to make some cash. I wished we didn't, but we were going dutch on twice-brewed coffee from the Dumpster and when that happens, you simply have no choice but to make some dough.

Despite our greatest efforts, we haven't yet learned to live without money. Maybe someday we'll find Sanity and she'll tell us how. If we figure out how to survive on the economy of the natural earth, and the impossibility of free energy becomes possible, I'll certainly let you know. You better believe I wouldn't keep something like that a secret. But until Utopia and her sister Peace come knocking on our door with all the answers like a pair of Mormon missionaries, we'll have to work.

It's pretty simple how we make money on the road. When we need some, we work. When we make enough, we move on. There's a term for people like us. They call us work opportunivores, formerly known as hobos. You see, hobos are traveling workers, and we're only hobos at select times of the year.

We'll take any job as long as we're desperate enough and it pays. Seriously, we're not picky. Just don't offer us any internships. None of those resume builders. We'll work and work hard if we can pocket quick cash and then dip outta the whole scene like two grinning wolves who have just tasted the blood of their kill.

◊ ◊ ◊ ◊

On a busy intersection in the mountains, opportunity presented itself in the form of a roadside stand. "Tree-Ripened Peaches," read the sign, and a huge light bulb switched on above my head. We peppered the woman running the stand with gunfire questions about the origin of her juicy peaches, biting into the samples and nodding approvingly. She told us about the small farm where those beautiful little peaches grew.

"Peach season's just begun," she said. "And the farmer's looking for harvesting help."

She scribbled a phone number onto the corner of a cardboard box and lent us her cell phone. We didn't waste a minute. After a few rings, a rough-sounding man came on the line. The owner of the orchard, Ted Shandy, gruffly told us he needed pickers tomorrow. He had a few solid weeks of work, if we liked work.

"You know, I'm not so big on work," I said. "But we're just about desperate enough to go there."

Ted's silence was frightening. "I don't like jokers," he said. "I like workers."

"Oh, I wasn't joking," I assured him.

"Come by this afternoon," he said. "We'll need to talk before you hit the orchard."

The afternoon we arrived at Shandy's Orchard, an oppressive heat baked the land. J.R. and I walked across a grassy pasture encircling a modest house. Four head of Hereford cattle milled nearby, swishing their tails like high-fashion skirts. The peach trees sagged heavy with fruit, and I could see our potential work on their branches.

At the door, Ted shook our hands with a muscular force that matched his voice. He invited us into his prefab, saddles on the porch and canning jars stored in wicker baskets on the windowsills. Ted was a thin man who sported a worn straw hat and round glasses. He spoke through a thick mustache and probably never took off his blue jeans, not even to shower.

J.R. and I sat at Ted's kitchen table as he brewed coffee. National Rifle Association magnets dotted the refrigerator like scales on a lizard, and a frozen meatloaf defrosted on the counter. Ted told us his son-in-law was a born-again Christian and that bothered the hell out of him. He told us the Muslims and Russians were after us and America was screwed. He told us he hated immigration. He hired Mexicans, he said, because that's who did the work happily. He'd rather hire us. He wished his kids would help him in the orchard, but they'd left the plow in the field for jobs in the town. That was the history of America according to Ted Shandy.

"It's the downfall of America, too," he said. "Lack of work ethic."

"Naw, the American work ethic is alive and well," I told him. "It's simply misdirected. Going toward things like overly technical outdoor gear and waterparks and minting pennies. Now that's the downfall of America. Waterparks and the GDP. Also throwing away food. Have you ever seen the dark side of a Monday evening Dumpster?"

Ted stared sideways as he sat at the table, like I was the evening news turned on during his vacation, so I shut up.

"I'm going to conduct a little interview, if you don't mind," he said, sipping coffee out of a silver thermos, a battle brewing like a storm in his irises. I liked the way that coffee sounded going through his mustache, but with the mood he was in, I wouldn't dare tell him so. We settled into the interview, armed, as usual, with every ounce of honesty we had.

"Do you drink?" he asked.

"Yes, yes." I assured him. "We go through a lot of water. Good to stay hydrated and all."

"Do you smoke?"

"He took up smoking just recently," I said, pointing to J.R. "But let's not talk about it. It's been a tough time for him, really it has."

The farmer shot us a rocket's red glare, as though our honesty had rubbed him the wrong way.

"Just to tell you ahead of time," he said, taking another noisy sip of coffee, "I prefer drinking over smoking dope. Drinking makes men angry but they still work, and work all day for that matter. And the work is what I care about, see?"

"To each his own," I said. Another glare from Ted.

"The dope smokers are the ones who drive me to drinking. Those guys only pick a couple baskets over a ten-hour shift. They never see another day in my orchard. You understand?"

"Yes, sir."

◊ ◊ ◊ ◊

We set up a temporary labor camp, parking Sunshine under a tall cottonwood tree. We'd stay there for the duration of the harvest. Not far from our camp was a one-bedroom house where a man named Harvey lived alone, tending his small cattle herd, cutting alfalfa, and raising rabbits. Harvey was the original owner of the property, but he sold to Ted and moved into the small house when his wife passed. Now, Harvey was eighty-five years old and danced at the Elks Club twice a week. He'd bought his '55 Ford pickup new, and liked to say he'd drive it straight into his grave. He sold us beef from his cattle for a dollar fifty a pound and a whole rabbit for ten dollars. During the harvest, we ate like kings.

One evening, after a twelve-hour shift picking peaches, we sat with Harvey over cold cans of Coors Banquet. The sunset radiated above us and the sky was so well illuminated we could barely look each other in the eyes. It was quiet for a while, only the rustling of the overhead leaves stirring around us. Then Harvey cleared his throat.

"What're you kids running from anyway, out on the road like that?" he asked. "Don't your families know where you are?"

I was surprised. By the sound of his voice, he didn't intend his words to be biting, but they seared through me hot. They churned up some of the deepest scars I have.

"We're not running from anything, Harvey," I said in a measured voice. "We're running *toward* something."

I wasn't sure he'd understand about the hot springs, so I didn't bring them up. We were all silent for a moment, and it was apparent that Harvey was dissatisfied with my answer.

I tried again. "Harvey. We're on an endless search for Sanity."

I said it so dead serious that it struck some chord in Harvey. He cracked up, a sight everyone should see sometime, an eighty-five-year-old man with five missing

149

teeth, wearing a John Deere trucker's hat, losing it like a little kid watching Looney Tunes. His laughter was so comfortable and familiar, it felt like I'd known him my whole damn life. Well, his hilarity spread to J.R. and he was losing it, too, and then I started in. Together, we laughed and laughed until tears burned our cheeks and the sky dimmed its bright lights and the first stars came out to tell us about eternity.

Then we stamped on our Coors cans and said goodnight in the dark. J.R. and I crawled into the upstairs bed of Sunshine and listened to the murmur of Harvey's old television set in the still night.

"You know what?" I asked J.R.

"What?"

"I think I heard Sanity tonight."

We didn't talk about it beyond that, but I meant what I said. Sanity had climbed the thick branches of the cottonwood tree when we were laughing. She laughed, too, and I don't know if anyone else would believe it, but one of her tears fell on my forehead. ◊

Peach Pickin'

Picking peaches isn't so bad, as far as work goes. Believe me, we've had worse jobs, like that time we dug gravel out of a fountain with short-handled shovels for six weeks. Or that time I was part of a test audience for romantic comedies. That was one of the toughest jobs I've had. You try sitting in a dark theater in your favorite sweater, listening to two beautiful people murmur about love. If that's not a cure for insomnia, I'm a fucking camel who delivers gold.

Toughest part about picking peaches is the itch. You know that fuzz peaches wear like a fine suit? Eat one peach and you don't notice too much that the peach dressed up for the occasion. But touch thousands of peaches in a day, and you realize at peach six hundred and twenty two that the peaches don't necessarily enjoy you fondling their fine suits. The fuzz, you see, is an armor. It sheds and runs down your shirt, agitating your neck and belly and every single inch of your skin. The fuzz is invisible, but you feel it like your disapproving aunt at Thanksgiving dinner, relentless aggravation in all the places you can't reach to scratch.

Second toughest part about picking peaches is the heat. The noontime sun beams down, and even in the shade of the orchard you're looking at temperatures over one hundred. Migrant labor isn't for the faint of heart, but I've already told you why it suits our lifestyle. No one wants you to stick around after the last peach has been picked, and that's just fine with us. We wanna pick, sleep, collect our cash, and resume our tramping life on the beat up road.

A typical morning at Shandy's Orchard starts at 4:30 a.m. That's coffee time. Or beer, if it's that kind of morning. Or some other drug, if it's *that* kind of morning, only don't tell Ted and don't allow your eyes to get one bit bloodshot or else Ted'll kick you out of the orchard for good. Really, he wasn't kidding about that. He escorted a kid off his property once, just for having too much sugar before his shift. Good thing we have bacon for breakfast.

By 5:00 a.m., all of the Shandy's Orchard employees are in the packing barn, folding up shipping boxes like God's Skeleton Construction Crew. I've always thought that God must have a team putting together human and animal skeletons before they're covered with skin like paper maché and sent out into existence. In my mind, they always looked like us here, standing in the early dawn folding up boxes, yawning and telling dirty jokes in Spanish while cardboard sounds squeak through the air.

Ted hires eight employees for harvest. That's four pickers and four sorters. J.R. picks alongside Ted and three guys from Chihuahua, Mexico. I sort and pack peaches alongside Maria from Guadalupe and her twelve-year-old son, Fernando. He may be a kid, but he's a damn hard worker. The other sorter, Nate, is seventeen and dropped out of school at fifteen. He works at the Greyhound station by night, grabs a to-go coffee, and shows up for his shift at the orchard fueled by caffeine.

The Spanish station, 106.5 Juan, plays all day from an ancient boombox on the ground. It's a mix of cumbia, reggaeton, and mariachi folk songs. When you do work like this, your brain switches to overdrive, spinning in spirals. Sometimes it carries you to places you don't wanna visit, so the music provides needed relief.

Nate, the caffeine-fueled dropout, talks to his baby-mama on speakerphone as we sort. It can be hard to tell what to believe about Nate, but one thing is obvious: he isn't a fan of 106.5 Juan Radio. He blasts Insane Clown Posse over the mariachi horns, trying in vain to cancel them out. The heavy metal converges with Juan Radio in a twisted sort of culture clash, the type America thrives on. Nate believes that America's shoddily constructed out of conspiracies. I say he's a Pessimist caught up in the pointless war of truth versus fiction, but then maybe I should keep dangerous thoughts like that to myself.

Mateo's been working with Ted the longest, and he knows a lot about peaches. He knows a lot about agriculture in general, raised on his family's ranch down in Chihuahua. He lives in the loft of Ted's whitewashed packing barn year round, because his family's still down in Mexico. One morning, Mateo invited us over to his place above God's Skeleton Construction Crew. He showed us photos of his family, taken on his most recent visit home. I asked Mateo what he thought of America.

"She's nice. A lot like Mexico," he said.

The first day we met Mateo, he showed up drunk on the job, smelling like a barroom floor and looking like he'd just woken up on one. He got his unlicensed Toyota stuck in the irrigation ditch on the south side of the orchard. Then, slurring his words somewhere between English and Spanish, he stalked over to the barn.

Ted followed him, saying, "Mateo, come on man. I know it's not so bad. It's never so bad."

Ted repeated that statement for forty-five minutes, folding boxes under Mateo's loft, until Mateo came down clutching a Budweiser in each hand and wordlessly offered one to Ted. Ted accepted the cold can and cracked it open. The sound was like the breaking of bread at communion. Mateo swayed, and for a moment I was afraid he might punch Ted in the face. Instead, he opened his beer and held it to Ted, offering a toast.

The cans clinked together like an introduction to the National Anthem, because they were Fourth of July Edition Buds and everything, including Mateo's slurred English, was streaming through the morning like red, white, and blue. J.R. and I went back to work while Ted and Mateo sat in the shade, drinking their beers in silence. Finally, Ted guided Mateo to his hayloft bedroom and returned to the orchard alone. He told us Mateo would sleep it off and tomorrow he'd be fine. After that, it was tough for me to believe anything Ted said about immigration.

Two days later, Mateo was sober as a sparrow, flitting through the understory of the orchard like an employee who'd received news that the lottery drew in his favor. Ted wandered between the four peach pickers, looking into their baskets for quality control.

"Grande Rojo, Grande Rojo," Ted chanted, grabbing an underripe peach from J.R.'s basket and pitching it at his leg. Grande Rojo was the catchphrase of Shandy's Orchard. Ted sang it tirelessly throughout the entire workday, like a chickadee saying its own name. It meant "big, red," just the way he liked his peaches, and I'll be damned if those silly syllables didn't cycle through my sleep like grammar on a turntable.

"Grande Rojo!" Mateo echoed.

J.R. winked at me, in the mood for poking at Ted. "Chico, Verde!" he said. "Chico, Verde, Teddy!" *Small, green.*

Ted rolled his eyes. "What a wiseass. You keep that up and we'll feed ya to the Russians."

Around 6 p.m., we called it quits. The trailer was loaded so heavy with fruit that I expected it to break in two. My legs ached, sweat pooled behind my knees, and my neck itched like wool sweaters in an Indian summer. Most of us climbed onto the back of the trailer, behind the tall stack of boxes, to ride back to the barn. Mateo and his buddies rode in Mateo's Toyota, too proud to ride on the back of the trailer, following some hierarchy I didn't understand.

As the trailer bumped down the peach rows, Maria's son Fernando stood above us, spreading his arms to their full wingspan, a dove flying in the wind. Maria watched him, smiling and scratching her forearms, itchy from the peach fuzz. I joined Fernando in his airborne shenanigans, extending my arms till my chest ached. I closed my eyes and pretended I was a hawk catching an evening thermal. Fernando tapped my shoulder, pointing up.

Sure enough, circling above us was a bald eagle. Fernando and I flapped our wings desperately, wanting nothing more than to transcend our heavy human bodies. If only we could lift off from the trailer, maybe we'd be free as that eagle. Maybe we'd never have to work again.   ◊

FOOTPRINTS OF SANITY

First time I stared a moose straight in the eye was in the thick innards of the Wenimuche Wilderness.

We hiked ten, twenty, thirty miles in, to some of the wildest country in the lower Forty-Eight, searching for long-lost pieces of ourselves. The easy cadence of my footsteps set the pace for my musings. At one point, I lost my identity. No longer was I separate from the outside world. Rather, I became the sights and smells around me. Whatever sensory information entered my doors of perception transformed me into the forest. I became a true child of the woods. I became a child of America.

It was a particularly warm day, and we decided to take it slow and hike six miles. The woods spit the trail into an emerald meadow, then swallowed it whole all over again.

I felt his eyes on me the moment I stepped into the shade of a stand of aspens, a big bull moose lounging in a puddle. From thirty yards away, I smelled the ripe scent of his wild vivacity. He was slicked with mud and his posse of flies gave wind to the still air. Our eyes connected like the cue ball clicking the eight ball in a close game of billiards.

"You gonna move?" he asked.

"No. You gonna move?" I asked.

No threats. Just two disconnected souls rejoined by the vulnerable intimacy of eye contact.

The presence of the moose brought my attention to my own strange human conventions. I grew self-conscious about my backpack, my hiking shoes, the bandana in my hair. Why, if I stood out there naked as him, I'd be just as much part of the earth. I'd be just as connected, one with the flies and the itch and the stink of being alive. So I did just that. I shed my clothes and stood before the moose on equal terms. Now we could talk.

"Hey," I said. "Do you know of a place called Tangerine Hot Springs?"

"No. Can't say I've heard of it. I don't usually spend time in places with names. I think we're all better off unnamed and untamed and alive in these private corners of the woods."

He then wandered off to find a peaceful part of the woods to call his own, nameless though it was.

I realized as he plodded away that I'd forgotten to ask him about Sanity. But that was ok. The moose, he was right. We are still wild creatures and we belong out here. These wild places are our homes. Don't you ever forget that, dear reader. We are unbridled souls meant to live free.

We wandered the wilderness for six days after we saw the moose. At all times, we scanned the landscape for Sanity. It made perfect sense to me that Sanity would spend her time in these woods. Sure enough, we often stumbled upon signs of her, a hair on a low branch, the scent of churned earth in the air. We'd catch a faint giggle near an alpine lake or distinguish a lone footprint in the mud. Through all that, though, we still didn't run into Sanity herself.

The remainder of the week, we swam in lakes and foraged wild mint and basked in the joys of summer. We passed a grouse family scratching through a subalpine meadow, pecking at bluebells. They spooked before I could speak with them. Later that day, a pine marten bounded through the woods, slinky and athletic. He was too fast to flag down for a proper conversation. Finally, we caught up to a marmot couple as they taught their young to forage.

"Have you seen America?" I asked the marmots.

"Oh yes," they said. "She's over on the West Fork, doing trail maintenance. They've got her on dynamite this year."

But they, too, left before I got to ask them about that elusive spirit of the forest.

I often wonder if moose think about things like Sanity. I wonder if they ever see her up there in their swampy haunts. I've seen confined animals plagued by a madness similar to the madness I saw in myself and the television screen and all the people around me back in the megacity, but I didn't know if wild animals ever experienced the same concerns. I told J.R. I needed more miles on the trail to cure

I need the wild the way I need food or love or sleep.

me from thoughts like that. I told him we should follow the mysteries of a rarely used trail while the weather still held us in her favor.

We hitchhiked to town and resupplied with nine days of food. Then, sitting at the trailhead, we decided to hike the length of the Grouse Mountain Trail, one hundred back-country miles. It turned out to be the right decision, because on our third day hiking Grouse Mountain Trail, we ran into the famous naturalist John Muir. The resemblance was so uncanny that we stopped him to say, "Hey, you look like John Muir!"

"That's because I am," said John Muir.

"It's nice when things are what they appear to be," said J.R.

John Muir wore a sweat-wicking shirt that bore the science of an entire space-ship. His shorts were designed for ultimate cooling, and his backpack only weighed in at fourteen pounds, incredibly light even stuffed full of food.

"Good speaking with you," John Muir said, "but I suppose I've got to be getting further up the trail. I've got fifteen miles left to hike today."

"Wait!" The word erupted out of me like a plea for life itself.

John Muir turned around. His eyes were white, spooked by my desperate demeanor.

"Please, if you don't mind, I've got a question for you."

John Muir extracted an energy bar from the outside pocket of his backpack and bit into it hungrily.

"All right, then. Shoot."

"Well, I've been wondering. Do moose ever think about Sanity? And, for that matter, do you ever see Sanity running through these mountains?"

"That's the first mention of Sanity I've heard in a long time," said John Muir. "No one I know talks about her much anymore. Back in my Yosemite days, Sanity lived at the foot of present-day El Capitan. Ansel Adams once took a photo of her there, but that photograph hasn't been seen by anyone in years."

On cue, J.R. drew his camera like a pistol and shot a portrait of John Muir.

"Anyway," Muir continued, "I moved out of California. Too many people for me. I haven't seen Sanity in a long time, though I catch signs of her every once in awhile. And, I'm sorry to say, I don't know what moose think about Sanity at all. They're rather quiet, and I wouldn't want to put words in their mouths."

"But where do you think Sanity is now?" I asked him.

"You want to know what I really think about it?"

"Do I ever!"

"Sometimes I think that Sanity's just Insanity dressed up for the fun of it," he said. "But, really, I don't know any more about it than that."

John Muir shrugged and clipped the buckle on his pack. He thanked us for not asking him to autograph our backpacks, as he said so many hikers do. Then he set off down the trail sprightly as a deer, leaving us to wonder about that picture of Sanity at the base of El Capitan and what exactly Ansel Adams was hiding from us all. ◊

Everything fades.
Life is transient.
It's tragic.
But you know what?
It's also why
The world is
So heartbreakingly
beautiful

THE SALMON KING

From my first glimpse of the Salmon King, I could tell he was my kind of bum. The old man stood on the shoulder of the road, his thumb out like the Big Dipper pointing to the North Star. I pulled over to offer him a ride, wondering where he got the insulated onesie he wore. It protected his body from the cold like an army of nylon soldiers.

The old man's walk was like a wheelbarrow left out in the rain. His weathered skin revealed a life of hard traveling, and his beard blew in the wind like a flag for Vietnam veterans.

"Say," said the old man. "It's only another day and would you believe I haven't yet committed a crime? What about you kids?"

I shot my BB gun at a road sign. "Lawlessness is the most orderly way of life there is!"

The man looked at J.R., his eyes supple with consolation. "She looks like a handful," he said.

I wondered why I couldn't just look like myself.

The old man motioned to a broken dog attached to the broken dog leash he held. She was a mutt with eyes sterile as a doctor's office and a tail stiff as a radio antennae.

"This is Cherry," he said. "And I am the Salmon King. But, please, call me Harry."

J.R. shook the old man's hand firmly. "Please, Salmon King, come in," he said. "Welcome to our humble abode."

The Salmon King made himself comfortable amidst our stuff in the backseat and his dog Cherry curled up on the floor. Freedom sat beside Harry, chatting up a tornado. The Salmon King told us, first off, that he'd once been a cop.

"Worst two days of my life," he said.

"Two days?" I asked.

"Yes, well. Somehow, I went through twelve pairs of handcuffs in one night. When I called the boys at the station to ask for a thirteenth, they lost their marbles. I didn't last another day."

We took Harry the Salmon King to his camp in the woods, the royalest bum's camp I'd ever seen. His Winnebago rose from the forest floor like a castle. Beside it was a green Dollar Delite tent spray-painted with some familiar words: "Cops are heads and decency is dead." I felt right at home.

"Your camp is a tangerine dream," I told the Salmon King.

"How long have you been set up here?" J.R. asked him.

"Long enough to know it's the only place for me."

By the looks of his camp, he'd been living in this corner of the woods for years. I could see why. It was a secluded camp, away from the road, the river playing like a radio below. I admired the Salmon King for setting up a stationary hobo camp. It didn't matter to him that as a bum, you're supposed to move around all the time. I guess some bums are braver than J.R. and me. Some bums have the guts to claim for themselves permanent camps in beautiful apline patches. Those unabashed warriors of Freedom and idleness are the people I admire most.

The people I love live life however they damn please. They take risks, they speak bluntly, they don't stay safe, because safe is boring and boring is worse than being dead. Sure, when you run forward fast as they do, you're bound to trip up and fall sometimes. But that doesn't keep them down. When they make mistakes, they pick their sorry butts back up smiling, because mistakes happen anyway. You gotta live the way you want and make no apologies. A life of insecurity is the only sure way to joy.

Harry opened the side flap of his Dollar Delite tent. "Why don't we go inside and get cozy in the master bedroom?"

"How come you don't stay in your RV?"

"Ah, too much stuff in there," he said. "You sure don't need to work to accumulate material wealth, kids. Just don't tell the Freedom from Want Party that. You know their whole cause is supplying the needy with their wants. If they know I'm overrun by stuff, that my wants are fulfilled, they'll feel useless! There's no point ruining their day with that, is there?" He winked and I could tell that ruining the FFW's day would be one of his greatest honors.

Harry's tent smelled of stale smoke and wet dog and dried urine. I almost knocked over a large shotgun propped up by the tent door. The ground glittered with shards of glass, so I was careful to pick my way over the junk and to a safe spot for sitting. It wasn't easy, as there were miscellaneous specimens of kitsch arched like a rainbow over the ground. Pots filled with rainwater, soggy books, food wrappers that looked like haikus, a photo of the Buddha propped on a stool, lit tea candles, and a tape recorder. The blankets we sat on had a texture like dried oatmeal.

J.R. entered carrying a trash bag full of stale doughnuts and, after we'd settled in, offered them to us. "These are a gift from Mother Dumpster," he said.

"How is she doing?" asked The Salmon King. "It's been a fucking long time since I saw Mother Dumpster."

"Modern trash compactors are displacing her left and right," said J.R.

"She's tries to joke about it," I said, "but everyone knows there's nothing sadder than a living anachronism."

"It makes me sick thinking about Progress turned loose in the world, transforming what's free into ugly captivity," said Harry.

"Just like what Insanity does to Optimism," I said.

"Orange Is Optimism, huh?" said the Salmon King. "Man, you kids. Such a throwback to the search for the New Age."

I continued, "Insanity fools everyone into thinking they need to work—" I stopped myself. "Oh, but you know all about living free. I saw how well you and Freedom get along."

"Freedom's a friend of mine because I harbor no Fear," said the Salmon King. "That's the manifesto of the kingdom I'm building. Kids, I am sanctioning this piece of land to be put to my kingdom's use and I will tell you why."

And then, the Salmon King commenced telling his story.

"I was sixty-eight when I first laid eyes on this spot. I'd spent forty years hitch-hiking around the world with only my backpack and a heart full of anticipation. All I'd ever done was pass through places, trying to escape a fear that gnawed at my soul.

"That fateful day, under these aspens, I experienced a white-hot moment of enlightenment. I realized that living in fear was Insane! I knew it was time to stop running from fear. So I quit my tramping, and here I've remained ever since."

"You know about Insanity too?" I asked.

"That Insanity you speak of, she lives in places where Fear is harbored. You see, most people don't know how to live free of Fear. But here, in my corner of the woods, I'm building a kingdom where Fear can be vanquished for good.

"Kids, the Freedom from Want Party has it all wrong. Freedom from want isn't true Freedom, because want can never be extinguished. That's where the FFW messes everything up. Fear is what we should battle, not want. This will be a place where bums like us can live free of Fear!"

The longer we sat in that tent listening to the Salmon King, the more paranoid I became that all he owned was that pathetic hairless dog and filthy backpack. A spectral mood settled over me, an incisive hunch that we were sitting by a murdered man's Winnebago, smoking his stash from his ashy bong, and lounging on his urine-stained bedsheets. I had no proof backing my hunch, but I entirely expected a hostile ghost to pop in the window any moment, shouting "Bums! Bums! Get outta here, you squatters!"

Harry was boiling water on a portable backpacking stove, a flimsy thing. The kettle bubbled with the thermal fury of Old Faithful, its steam warming the tent. I took off my jacket and felt the flickering eyes of Harry focused on my chest. My hand instinctively rose to cover my orange amulet, but I was too slow.

"Well, Orange Is Optimism, after all. I should have known. You kids are looking for the hot spring, aren't you? You're the pilgrims they're all talking about! I didn't think you'd arrive until next spring. But here you are."

"You know about the hot springs?" I asked.

"Are you kidding? That's why I'm here, baby! I've got them all to myself. With all I've been through in life, I deserve it."

"Do you have an amulet?"

"Not anymore. I got a gun instead. Keeps Fear away better than any amulet."

"Never mind Fear," I said. "Have you ever seen Sanity?"

"Sanity?" Harry's eyes were two stars in the center of a burning American flag. "Last time I saw Sanity, I went blind for three days. It took a good dose of government-sanctioned political propaganda to recalibrate me to my normal state."

In a sudden tremor, the Salmon King went limp, as though he'd misplaced his skeleton. He looked like a stolen sack of cash in the trunk of a Buick. Cherry exploded with a howl, and J.R. shook the Salmon King violently.

"Are you having a heart attack?" he demanded.

But the Salmon King didn't answer. I didn't know why. It didn't seem you'd need a skeleton to speak.

I was mildly worried we would witness the Salmon King's death. Only the whites of his eyes showed, and he did look gruesome, but, still, I wondered if he hadn't purposefully left his body behind only to instill Fear into us, as a lesson.

Turned out Harry's perfect smile was false as manufactured scarcity. His perfectly white dentures fell halfway from his mouth. They flapped open and shut as though they were giving a commencement speech. Sadly, the wordless chatter of the false teeth was a grossly familiar sight. Most people who open their mouths have about as much to say as the Salmon King's dentures did.

What transpired next was more woeful than the deplorable state of Harry's limp body in J.R.'s arms. As he tried to rouse the pitiful Salmon King from his stupor, J.R. clumsily rammed his elbow into the portable stove. The stove, still aflame, spun through the air like a shiny new coin, then crashed quite elegantly into the side wall of the tent, which instantly erupted into flames.

Cherry ran outside. J.R. brazenly beat at the fire with a t-shirt and a spatula. I poured a bottle of piss over the flames. It's what was close by. Despite our efforts, we couldn't compete with the fire's haste. It voraciously consumed the side wall of the tent as an appetizer, then hungrily moved onto its main course: the ceiling.

Overwhelmed by the ardent heat and voluminous smoke and pure prick of panic, J.R. and I aborted the mission. We each seized one of Harry's flaccid legs and dragged him out through the tent opening into a soft pile of leaves. We coughed and wheezed, sucking oxygen into our lungs to cleanse them from the heavy smoke. The air smelled like the corpse of the tent, and I cried a little as it went down. I'm always saddened by the incredible force of entropy.

J.R. and I watched as the tent burned like all our good intentions. Harry lay inert on the cold ground, looking like a dry spring as Cherry licked his sooty face. Just as I was about to ask J.R. what we should do about Harry, the old man sat up in the leaf litter easy as an oil change, as though he'd never collapsed in the first place. We fearfully apologized for the awful accident, apprehensive about the Salmon King's reaction.

"Oh, it doesn't matter much," he said. "I'll just get another from the Freedom from Want Party. If you don't get something from them every few months, they'll think you have no wants and there's nothing to set you free from. Then I'll have to take to working to survive!""

He brushed his hands and turned away. "Well, we'll stay here a bit. Make sure this inferno doesn't get out of hand. Plus, I haven't built a good fire in a while. We should tell Dollar Delite their tent provides a good heat."

We stood there in silence as the tent crackled and smoke billowed through the trees. A raven flew overhead, checking out the action with curiosity.

"You know," said the Salmon King, "if I were you two, I wouldn't spend so much time searching out Sanity. If you find her, you'll probably be forced to get a steady job. Hell, all my life I've been lighting fires on the refuse of Insanity. I wouldn't ever dream she'd go away. If she does, I just might freeze."

He rolled a spliff and smoked it as though it were the very thoughts from his head. When the flames on the tent quieted, he turned to us.

"Enough of this. Are you two ready? We're going to the healing waters, kids." ◊

Freedom from Fear

In order to reach the Salmon King's hot spring, we had to cross a deep river that tinkled like a pop song under our feet. When J.R. and I arrived, Harry was already nude and soaking, steam rising around him to the skies like all my most sacred dreams.

The spring itself consisted of a pink kiddie pool fed by a duct-taped conglomeration of chipped white plastic that would only resemble pipes to a retired plumber. The water was deep enough to cover half of Harry's buttocks and his feet, minus the higher altitude of his big toe. The sores on his body, now visible, were the same color as the fall leaves, all yawning yellows and tired reds.

J.R. and I shed our clothes right away, cold and eager for a soak in the spring, never mind that it was only a plastic pool. When we sank into it on either side of Harry, most of the water rushed over the shallow edges. An inch and a half of lukewarm water was all that remained.

"Hey, you explorers picked up some wounds on your way over, didn't you? You're in good company. Columbus, he had his worries too. You think he had Band-Aids out there in the middle of the Atlantic?"

"I have a lot in common with Christopher Columbus," I told him. "We're both mislabeled fools. That's what happens when you're an Optimist, I guess."

"You kids and Optimism," said Harry. "Kills me."

I could see why the Salmon King was capable of founding his own kingdom, because Pumpkin Hot Spring belonged to him! Who cared if it smelled like rotten fish? Who cared if it was covered by a film of black muck?

We soaked in the shallow water, chilly for sure, but happy. Never mind the cold air. Never mind the slime. The sun was bright and the sky was blue and I couldn't imagine a more noble position to be in than this, seeker of a holy hot spring.

"Good thing I warded off the Freedom from Want Party," said Harry. "Can you believe that every Friday they'd waste an entire day working on the spring? They think hard work will fix every problem in the world."

"The FFW used to run the spring?" asked J.R.

"They maintained it for the needy," said Harry. "Anyone could soak here, anyone at all. A wonderful, utopian vision, they had. That is, until the place spiraled out of control and the regulations were posted. There were so many rules, I couldn't stand it. I put that to rest quickly."

"How'd you do it?"

He pantomimed squeezing a trigger. "Told you guns work better than amulets. But really, kids, I wish you could've seen how horrible it was here."

The Salmon King smudged black algae onto his arms. "Everything's too civilized for my tastes nowadays. Nowhere left for Freedom. Since I took over, Pumpkin Hot Spring has returned to its former state. It's just the way it was in the sixties, before everything became a corporate cabaret. Everyone's lusting over the sexy goods of Capitalism. Not this old chap! If you want for nothing, you won't be trapped in the great cycle of want."

"It's true," said J.R. "Only fools think money can help them rise out of poverty."

"That's exactly what the FFW doesn't want you to know. But I've figured it out and so have you. We bums recognize that you'll never be happy if you receive everything you want. We know of the surplus today's machinery provides.

"They say you have to work hard to get what you want. Lies! All of them! We bums don't have to live in fear of so-called poverty. We don't have much money, sure, but money isn't real anyways. Look at all of *this*! This is what real. The best things in life are free, and anyone who thinks otherwise is living in *true* poverty."

"And poverty is a state of mind," I said.

"Couldn't have said it better myself," agreed the Salmon King. "Kids, I cannot believe the universe brought us together. Think of this grand opportunity."

"What opportunity?"

"I would like to invite you to join my Freedom from Fear Kingdom. We will aim to maintain a stronghold on this spring in order to protect our Freedom from Fear."

"But Freedom's right over there collecting leaves," I said.

"Never mind that," said the Salmon King. "I have a partner who is aiding me in the construction of the Freedom from Fear Kingdom. Our aim is to extinguish Fear by driving away those we fear. We will emancipate ourselves from the control of the FFW by gaining control of our own kingdom. This is a battle we must win! If we don't, we are doomed to live a life of subservience. We'll be slaves to Progress!"

"Fearful," said J.R.

"Here is the plan. First, we will erect a fence to deter our potential enemies. Then we will create sentry shifts, so we may watch for incoming members of the enemy groups. We will construct fortresses and stock a steady supply of ammunition."

"That sounds like a lot of work," said J.R.

"This is the antithesis of work! It's merely a radical strategy implemented by yours truly to destroy Progress and her ugly side effects once and for all."

"When I hear the word strategy, I think of work and war," I said. "Two concepts that make the heart of any seeker sick."

"If it doesn't contribute to Progress, it can't be work."

The Salmon King procured three parcels of foil from his backpack.

"Anyways I'm sure that with time, we will correctly arrange the colors in this shared rainbow. Why don't we break bread over our newfound alliance? Would you like a meatball sandwich?"

J.R. and I accepted the lunch with gratitude. We didn't agree with the tenets of the Salmon King's Freedom from Fear Kingdom, but how could we say no to such widely acclaimed submarine sandwiches?

"Say what you want about the FFW," said Harry, "they do make a tasty sub."

"These are tasty," said J.R. "You know, we never got to try one that day, Kit."

The Salmon King stopped mid-bite. "You visited the FFW?"

"Yeah," said J.R. "We heard rumors of their sandwiches and thought we could score some. Instead, they put us to work in some kind of parade for Capitalism. It was fun. We held signs and sang songs they even gave us costumes to wear. Look, I took a picture of Kit."

J.R. showed the Salmon King a photo of me wearing the Freedom Fred donkey costume, holding the "Hegemony Isn't the Enemy" sign.

"Kids, I understand now where you're coming from."

"The open road!" I said. "Same place as you!"

The Salmon King rose from the plastic pool, covered with black algae and trembling with a nervous fury.

"I knew the Freedom from Want Party would eventually want to battle for the name of Freedom."

"I'm not sure you understand," I said. "We find politics a bore!"

But the Salmon King wasn't listening.

"Parcel it out so everyone gets a piece, is that your plan? Reinstate every rule?"

"No," I said. "We just want to find Sanity."

"The FFW's wrong about equality," Harry continued. "Not everyone can, or should, have their wants fulfilled. I earned this hot spring because I chose to starve myself of wants, not because I worked hard for it.

"Look, I've deprived myself of luxuries for years and I plan to continue my underprivileged lifestyle for the rest of my days. The FFW can't impose its rules on me. I like being a bum, no matter what they say about me. I will not be caught in their cycle of want! I will not succumb to their Capitalist propaganda! I will not live in fear of poverty! I will use intentional poverty to my own advantage."

I exited the kiddie pool as Harry fretted, and J.R. shot photos of him under the aspens, which now crackled in black and white.

"Spies. Spies! I should have known. It was only a matter of time before the FFW would discover my plans for true Freedom. This wasn't how it was supposed to go. I didn't assemble my defenses in time, and now my beloved hot spring is to pay for my despicable misjudgments. Pumpkin Spring, oh Pumpkin Spring. God shed his grace on thee. Till selfish gain no longer stains the banner of the free."

The Salmon King's frantic pacing sounded through the woods like the stringy music of danger. He seemed to forget J.R. and I were there at all. That's how it is with fearful people. They're always afraid of something they forget to look out for.

"Excuse me, Salmon King," I said.

"What?"

"Well, I just wanted to say…I don't think it's so Optimistic to define Freedom the way you do."

The Salmon King's laugh iced over the fall leaves like the winter's first freeze.

"Besides," I continued, "has it ever occurred to you that feeling deprived is the way of the Pessimist? That won't get you far."

The Salmon King walked over to a large boulder. There, a dark arm materialized, presenting him with a small handgun.

"If you stay out of news and politics, you'll find many reasons to be an Optimist,"

said the Salmon King. "If you stay away from people, you'll find even more."

The owner of the mysterious arm then stepped out from behind his boulder. I'd recognize that scowl anywhere. It was Pessimism himself, familiar as though I'd seen him the day before. He marched to the Salmon King's side, staring at me with thoughts twisted into gruesome shapes. The Salmon King fingered his gun like a secret, one he just might tell if we made an impetuous move.

"This is my partner Pessimism. He is second-in-command in my Freedom from Fear Kingdom. He will help me carry out my plan. Right now he faces a less tenuous task—destroying you!"

"Don't fear," said J.R. "We have nothing to do with the FFW."

"Ha! That's exactly what people like you would say. I have no Fear. I only have the will to protect what's mine."

"I haven't known you for too long, friend," said J.R. "But you seem kind of scared to me."

"How dare you call yourselves seekers! You two aren't true bums. You're merely slaves to the modern cycle of consumption, fueled by your own Fear of poverty. A search for Sanity? That is Insane! I told you, discovering Sanity would ruin the very life we seek. We're living off the excess of Insanity. Why would you fuck all that up? I'm telling you, it's Optimism who fools people into passively giving up their beloved kingdoms. You encountered truth here, and you denied it as soon as it showed itself to you."

"Truth is a myth," I said.

Harry shot at the sky, a wild look in his eye. At the bang, a black cloud of flies clustered around the hot spring like a Sunday morning congregation. Thousands of them circled us, blocking out the sky and blackening the landscape. The flies amassed around Harry and Pessimism until we could barely see them anymore, eating at their festering sores like they'd consume them in their entirety.

The Salmon King swatted at the plague of flies with a vengeance. Cherry ran in endless figure-eights, snapping at the flies. In his foolish futile dancing, Harry's prized dentures flew from his wrinkled lips, spinning in a dazzling white display through the air and landing in the scummy water of the kiddie-pool hot spring. The false teeth sank below the black algae, leaving only lazy bubbles on the surface of the water.

"No!" Harry fell to his knees. The flies erupted into an explosion of erratic clouds.

For a moment, the whole world paused. Nothing moved but the flies, little planets of black that circled like glimpses into the inner workings of our dark and unknown solar system.

"Salmon King," I said. "You're wrong, you know. You're wrong about Optimism!"

Pessimism stood near the hot spring, laughing like the flies tickled him to death. Harry probed the ground for his gun.

"Get out of here, hypocrites! Cherry! Make them leave!"

We ran into the river stark naked, narrowly escaping Cherry's angry jaws. J.R. threw a large stick at her. When that didn't work, he kicked her in the ribs. In the exchange, a nice-looking piece of J.R.'s calf was sacrificed. His blood was the color of a cardinal, and it left little drips like footsteps behind him.

Harry was having an outright fit back there in the hot spring, wailing and throwing black algae into the air. We crossed the river swiftly, fearful of what would happen if the Salmon King found his gun through the mess of flies.

On the other side, safe in Sunshine, we flashed up the road, away from Pumpkin Hot Spring of Harry the Salmon King. J.R.'s calf bled profusely, the red streams catching on the vinyl of his seat. We didn't dare touch the lacerations, not with our fingers or our minds. They were deep, but the mildest of our concerns.

We'd never know what became of Harry, if he survived the congregation of flies or if he retained the rights to his spring. The residue of the black algae clung to me like a warning. An eerie feeling settled over me, like I was looking down a metal funnel into my own future.

Near the pavement, we slowed as a black bear crossed the road. She blinked at us through the windshield, her eyes a window to ancient knowledge. I imagined she was delivering us a message from Sanity.

I opened the door to the bus, wanting to ask the bear her intentions. However, at the snap of the door, the bear spooked and sprinted into the bushes, where she took refuge from us. J.R. and I exchanged knowing smiles. I pressed on the gas pedal and we drove out of there with the alacrity of renewed pilgrims, back on the road, nothing to say, our mood renewed by the presence of the bear who bore the news of Sanity. So what if we hadn't found Tangerine Hot Springs? Who needs a promised land when every moment is a miracle?   ◊

The survival of the SOUL depends on an unrelenting QUEST for an undiminished LiFE

Trouble is the King of Everything Fun

In the Valles Caldera, we set up camp near an impossibly vibrant stand of ever-greens. It was the height of elk season, and hunting camps dotted the base of Pajarito Mountain like wasp nests on the side of a suburban home.

Terry, one of the hunters, invited us over to share a venison steak under the stars. He built a fire that was as luminous as resurrected sunlight. The temperatures must've been slumming somewhere under five below that night, and Terry's bon-fire saved us from freezing. His Chinook trailer blocked the wind, which howled and wailed like tortured pain repressed by previous generations of untold grief.

Terry dished up the venison and some buttered rolls from the grocery store. We shared food and company, booze and warmth. It was a comfort to wait out the single-digit darkness with another earnest soul, another unsure seeker out in the wild searching for Sanity. We stared at the hungry flames and talked fire talk. You know how it is around a fire, how its glowing flame draws out of you all the deep dark scary secrets you'd never tell in broad daylight. Terry told us he wished his wife had come up with him, but she didn't like the rustic life.

"Isn't life a lonely proposition?" he asked.

Before we could answer, he changed the subject and stoked the fire with a thick lodgepole branch.

"Are you driving down the mountain tonight? If so, you'd best git. It's late."

"No, Terry, we're staying up here just like you," I said. "We've got way too much time and nowhere to be."

"Supposed to snow pretty good up here. That bus of yours doesn't have snow tires, does it?"

"Naw, but we'll be fine," J.R. said. "We've got Optimism in our bus."

"Wait a minute, you two aren't socialists, are you?"

It wasn't easy, but we convinced Terry that nothing was further from our minds than socialism.

"Optimism has nothing to do with politics," we assured him.

We navigated our way home by the pale blue light of the stars. We passed two rabbits that looked like melted snow and a herd of grazing elk that looked nervous.

"Keep that up tomorrow," I told them. "Terry's going to be dressed and on the trail at 4:30 a.m."

I didn't sleep a wink that night, even under the weight of no less than seven blankets, wearing all the clothes I owned. J.R. and I have no heat in the bus, because we hold firm to the conviction that discomfort is a crucial component of joyful living. Today's society is generally an overinsulated place, and we escape that. Sometimes that means we suffer. Mostly it means that when our five-gallon water bottle starts freezing solid, we really should scoot south.

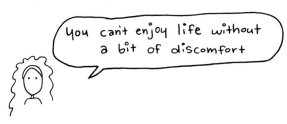

When we woke the next morning, fresh snow insulated the forest, cushioning its every sound. We ran through the powder as though we were children born to a world of white innocence, as though we'd never witnessed one cruel act or committed one evil deed, as though we lived in a virgin land of unpolluted wonder that would never be poisoned by a sinister soul.

Exhausted from the morning, J.R. and I retired to Sunshine. It was high time to figure out a plan for the winter, because I, for one, couldn't handle the mountains much longer, what with my sleep constantly compromised by subzero midnights that froze my toes.

J.R. was buried in his atlas for over an hour. He lit a cigarette and sucked it down with more finesse than I'd ever seen from him.

"As far as I see it," he said, "there are two options for us this winter. First is to head south and pick oranges. Second is incarceration."

186

"I'll go for number two," I said. "Name your crime of choice."

"It's between urban homelessness and insatiable curiosity, Both are overwhelmingly menacing to the government."

J.R. and I ate breakfast as the snow fell to earth like pieces of the sky. Another day, another view of America. I knew I'd never see those particular snowflakes fall again, and I knew the magic of the morning would dissipate soon. How miraculous it was to be sitting there at all. Sometimes I can't breathe in deeply enough. I want to inhale the world into my lungs. Sometimes every moment is so meaningful I could cry.

The afternoon elbowed its unwelcome way into the land of the free. I'd convinced myself that the cold would relent with its arrival. Instead, noon tick-tocked across the sky and still the temperatures crashed like an avalanche from the side of the mountain.

We realized, hit by a jolt of common sense, that if we didn't head down the mountain right now, we'd be stuck for weeks in a couple feet of powder. Sunshine skidded out of our campsite in a close call with friction and all its inherent problems. We careened down the dirt incline, deflowering its virgin snow. It was shameful to mar the perfect white scene that spread before us, but there we were, sliding on the corners and squinting through the foggy, slushy windshield.

"Careful!" J.R. hissed at me. "We're gonna topple over the edge!"

"Nah," I said as we slid ten feet down the road, the opposite way from how the steering wheel was turned. I didn't slow down one bit, beyond stopping at a whim for J.R. to take photos and grab another handful of snow to eat.

Halfway down the mountain, we stopped at a lodge to ask directions because it was likely we'd taken a wrong turn in the storm. I caught sight of a calendar on the wall. It was winter. Or fall. Or at least it wasn't summer. I knew that much. After a few moments, the symbols on the calendar clarified, like driving out of the snow. According to that calendar, it was December. The third week of December.

That meant the week before had been my sister's birthday. You know, I've never understood birthdays. Why celebrate something you can't remember? Why celebrate something when you haven't decided if it's a good or bad thing?

Last year, we visited Lady Liberty in New York. She's America's godmother, in case you don't know, a wise woman who barely anyone bothers talking about anymore. It was America's birthday and I told Lady Liberty my negative opinion of

I've searched so many places, only to find
the tall altitudes of the mind take me highest

festivities relating to natal exile.

"If you're gonna get in trouble," said Lady Liberty, "please don't let it be over something as trite as birthdays."

I thought of my sister at home, the sadness in her blue eyes the last time we'd said goodbye. I purchased a postcard for fifty cents and borrowed a pen.

WILLOW,

I THINK OF YOU ALL THE TIME IN YOUR TEENAGED PRISON. WANT TO RUN AWAY WITH ME? J.R. WOULDN'T CARE IF YOU TOOK THE DOWNSTAIRS. I SAW A DEER IN THE FOREST THIS MORNING AND SHE REMINDED ME OF YOU, HER CAREFUL MOVEMENTS, HER LONG GRACEFUL LEGS. I HOPE EVERYTHING'S OKAY BACK THERE.

I KNOW YOU'RE A YEAR OLDER, BUT I ALSO KNOW THAT DOESN'T MEAN THAT MUCH. I KNOW YOU DON'T LISTEN TO MUCH OF WHAT I SAY. JUST KNOW THAT I GET YOUR LETTERS, EVEN IF I DON'T ANSWER. KNOW IT'S NOT YOU. IT'S JUST THAT BIRTHDAYS HAVE ALWAYS BEEN A TOUGH THING FOR ME. I THINK EVERY DAY IS SPECIAL, AND EVERY DAY IS. I LOVE YOU. I DO. I JUST DON'T SHOW IT IN THE WAY YOU'RE SUPPOSED TO. ONE DAY I'LL TELL YOU A STORY ABOUT THAT. BUT THERE'S NO SPACE HERE.

HAPPY BELATED BIRTHDAY FROM PAJARITO MOUNTAIN.

—KIT

I mailed the card from the sleepy post office in town. Lady Liberty winked at me from the thirty-two-cent stamp, saying "Good job, you did that like a champ" and "Trouble is the king of everything fun." She waved goodbye as I dropped the postcard into the slot. Outside, the snow glittered like a thousand tiny eyes on the ground. ◊

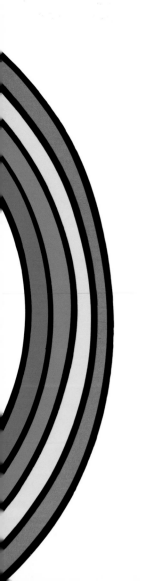

THERE IS NO
ROAD MAP
TO NOW

Broke & Brokedown

The Sangre de Cristo Mountains loomed to the south, warning us not to come near. To continue, we faced a tenuous task. A steep pass, riddled with ice, blocked us from our southbound route to Texas and its promise of warmth. I wrestled with the ornery steering wheel, my mittens wrapped tight around its unwieldy circumference.

Eight inches of heavy, fluffy snow had fallen like Western poetry the other night. The deep drifts had iced over in the subzero morning, and now they traced the road in frozen tracks, four neat lines of sharp ice twisting across the mesa top.

It was my current duty, as driver of the *USS Sunshine*, to accurately trace our tires over the tracks carved out by previous vehicles. It was quite a chore, harrowing, because Sunshine's undercarriage cleared the windrow in the middle by no more than three fingers.

I swooped over the road in deep concentration. That particular stretch must have been designed by some kind of dancer or musician. I found a waltz in its curves and surrendered to its romantic three-beat.

J.R. was slumped over in the passenger's seat, snoring. Some kind of sidekick. At least he had enough sense to snore in rhythm, as though even in his deep sleep he could hear the piano tunes. Together, conscious and unconscious, we enjoyed the recital peacefully, gratefully, so in tune with the road that we felt its potential velocity in our ventricles.

That's when a hook in the icy road criminally assaulted the bus by sneaking upon its driver unaware. The waltz from moments before abruptly transitioned into the chaotic synthesized music of modern times. A trip-hop beat dropped over the slow-motion disaster.

"Lift your foot off the brake," J.R. rapped. "Turn into the slide!"

It was dazzlingly tragic to watch the pretty afternoon spin out from under us and into a pile of exclamation points and eighth notes, all the rules of music and physics bent and stacked up. I closed my eyes and waited for Sunshine to plunge over the steep ledge, completely out of my control.

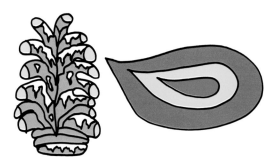

I was contemplating the problems of the world at large while J.R. investigated the deep inner workings of our filthy two-liter engine.

Most of the time we keep the door to the engine compartment shut, but today, that wasn't an option. Something was gravely wrong, and I knew there was nothing in my knowledge base to rescue us from our predicament.

Sunshine gushed oil like heavy tears of the apocalypse, and it coalesced into an ugly iridescent puddle on the snowy road.

"Instead of in the engine where it should be," J.R. muttered. "An environmental disaster, all this oil."

"What's wrong? What's wrong with the engine?" I asked, skating on the slick sheet of ice like a circus fool late to lunch.

"Give me a minute, Kit, and I can figure it out, okay? I'm looking in here for my coveralls." A bright red rope of licorice candy dangled from J.R.'s lips. "Why don't you try to do something helpful instead of buzzing around in my ear?"

My body boiled so hot I bet I could've melted the snow beneath my feet.

"Who got us into this mess?" I asked. "Who wanted to drive up to the tip-top of the mountain to watch the pretty snow as it fell? Who said no to finding work earlier this fall?"

"Calm down. I'm positive I can patch it up. Just give me some space, okay?"

From his workstation under the bus, J.R. told me we'd busted open a hose on the external oil cooler.

"How'd that happen?" I asked.

"High ice in the middle of the road probably," he said. "That goddamn oil cooler. I shoulda took that thing off when we got Sunshine. It's awarded us nothing but heartache from day one."

J.R. told me that the hose had cracked near the edge of a clamp. By his estimations, he figured he could cut the hose and refasten it cleanly in under an hour. He ducked under the bus again, armed with his pocket knife and a chattering smile. Promised we'd be on the road again in no time.

I sat on the ground near J.R., reading aloud from our VW Bible, *How to Keep Your Volkswagen Alive*. It's a compleat idiot's guide to mechanics, a manual heavy as my right leg, and we read its wise words whenever we find ourselves in a pickle like that. It has a lot of spelling errors, that book, but you know, I guess spelling doesn't matter much in the physical world.

"Kit, you're as redundant as money in the wild world of nature reading me that book, " J.R. told me.

So I quit my futile attempts to help J.R. and sat in Sunshine, protected from the wind. Time crept by noticeably, which was unusual for an idler such as myself. I tidied our silverware drawer, all two forks and two spoons and one wooden spatula we had.

I had faith J.R. would fix the hose, but the conditions were appalling: no lift, lying on the frozen ground in a puddle of oil. Optimism lay under the bus with him, doling out her best advice. Mechanical issues were her specialty, because after all, what is mechanics but the transformation of hunks of steel into a horseless carriage? If that isn't proof that the impossible can become possible, I don't know what else is.

I knew J.R. offered sweet gratitude to Optimism from the depths of his amateur mechanic's heart, because, at the very least, we both knew her company was what maintained any semblance of an orange glow about the steely afternoon.

The accident had occurred on a pleasingly voluptuous back road that undulated through the sage and rabbit burrows. It was shamefully underused. Not one other vehicle passed us the entire day, probably because the driving conditions weren't ideal, as we'd proven through our misfortune.

The sun shone bright, but the true temperament of the day was frigid as a legal document. Our old thermometer didn't rise above twenty-five degrees, not even at noon. A wind blew from the north, a cruel wind, sadistic and unrelenting. With wind chill, it was absurd to think you could retain your body temperature at its normal 98.6 degrees.

No matter how deep I buried my mittens into my pockets, my hands still burned with the cold. They puffed up, large and red and aching, but nothing like J.R.'s. To work on the hose, he needed bare hands, unencumbered by protective sheaths. When I touched them, they felt like a chain-link fence on Christmas Day.

Periodically, J.R. clambered from his frozen prison and joined me for a short respite in the bus. His coveralls hung from his body, wet with melted snow. Though his countenance remained light, he was silent as the mountains themselves.

We did what we could that afternoon. I kept the kettle burning over our propane stove, heating water to pour over J.R.'s aluminium hands. They would solidly freeze to the marrow until he could barely wiggle his fingers anymore, and the hot water restored some vigor to them, at least.

After one round of hot-water hand-warming, a metallic sound, like gold teeth chewing up nickels, tore through the cold air. J.R. was having an outright fit, saying words that would skin a cat and throwing his wrenches on the ground. Optimism ran off into the sage, terrified by his outburst.

"What's wrong?" I asked, sensing danger in the tremble of his cold voice.

"The hose is too short! I can't fucking clamp it on. I've been trying for hours, but it's not gonna work, Kit. It just can't work. I can't make the hose longer."

He kicked Sunshine's tire with the pure energy of cold and tired freezing frustration. It was a forceful kick, and the inertia of the motion worked with the slippery pavement in such a way that he flew through the air like a raven on the wing, then landed with a thud on a hard patch of ice.

Now, I wanted to be sympathetic, because I was sure that impact was tough on both his skeletal frame and his ego. But it was so comical, I doubled over as J.R. lay there on the ice like the catch of the day at a fish market, his brow furrowed over the dire situation.

Laughter is a release of our deepest carnal fears, and the catharsis of it felt good, especially when J.R. joined in. Then, he rolled over onto a soft patch of snow and stared at the sky. His sudden solemn expression erased my momentary mirth.

After all, when I really considered our current dilemma, nothing was all that funny. Both J.R. and I harbored a painful awareness that we couldn't afford a tow. Money was always tight during winter, when picking jobs were scarce, and now it looked like we might not make it for citrus harvest. Also, we'd lost a good portion of our peach earnings in an episode I'd rather not discuss. It had something to do with an overpriced apple corer and a stranger from the Ukraine and the idea of drilling hot water from the core of the earth, but really I'd rather not talk about it.

"What in the name of candles and Frisbees are we going to do?" I asked J.R.

"Considering it's almost dark, I think we're going to warm up and cook some dinner and go to sleep."

We pushed Sunshine onto a straightaway. Right there on the shoulder of the road, we made our usual camping preparations. Since no one had driven by all day, we weren't much concerned that we'd be in the way, even parked right there on the white line.

Inside Sunshine, J.R. removed his oil-soaked coveralls. I poured another round of hot water over his hands and he splashed it up onto his face and neck, to wash off all the oil. It wasn't the most successful hygiene session, but it worked well enough. We put on every article of clothing we owned to brace ourselves for the perilous night.

As the sun turned itself in and the temperatures crashed into us with single-digit depression, I cooked a soup out of some beef bones and potatoes. We ate quickly. J.R. looked so exhausted I thought he might fall asleep into his bowl, but he managed to make it through the meal by cracking a few lousy jokes. They didn't make me laugh much, even though they usually did.

We left our greasy bowls outside for the coyotes to lick clean. Then we transferred all our possessions from the trunk to the front seat. We'd have to sleep downstairs that night with the top down to retain heat. With the blankets, and our mutual offering of body heat, we didn't freeze, even though it was a cold night of glacial proportions. Our warmth, sufficient through those long hours, gave proof to the night that hope wasn't all lost.

Next morning, we woke to the same bright sun and the same ugly puddle of oil on the ground. I'd convinced myself, in my slumbering midnight delusions, that the previous day was only a sick nightmare orchestrated by Pessimism. Of course, that was a cruel joke. We were still stranded on a frozen road with no oil, no hose, and another freezing day ahead of us. Fooling myself was different than practicing Optimism. Believe me, I learned that lesson the hard way. You know, I'd realized I could learn a lot from myself, if I could get over what a jerk I could be.

Speaking of Optimism, she was jumping all over the place in the morning. What was her deal? I was busy melting snow in the kettle for coffee water when I heard it too: a muffled crunching like tumbleweeds trundling across the snow—that is, if tumbleweeds were heavy as cows.

The sound grew louder. It sounded like a trash compactor in a really good Dumpster. Like eternity going on vacation. It sounded like—

"A motor!" I poked my head out of Sunshine like a prairie dog. "J.R.! Some hero is braving this icy morning! They're nearing ground zero!"

The silence of the mesa was unimpeded, so much that the truck was still miles away when I first heard it. Our motorized savior was nowhere close. The crunching approached for ten endless minutes. Those ten minutes were like fast-forwarding my entire childhood on VHS, grainy, fuzzy, and vaguely familiar. Just when I was set to turn off the television set, a white Dodge Ram curved around the corner of the road like a Super Bowl commercial.

The truck halted beside Sunshine. The two vehicles stood abreast, stomping their feet and blowing into each other's nostrils just like horses on a dusty trail. A man emerged from the front seat, a faded blue-jean hero wearing custom cowboy boots made of rattlesnake. He gifted each of us a Styrofoam cup.

"It's just coffee," said the man. He was thrifty with his words and seemed to consider each one carefully before letting it slide through his lips. "I put some of that hazelnut creamer in it. Most folks don't like their coffee black."

I was amazed by all of it, the coffee and the truck and the kind eyes and the impossibly beautiful boots sticking out of those dirty blue jeans.

"My name's Kurt. That's my ranch over there." He pointed to the base of the snow-capped mountains. "I saw you here last night and wondered what the hell someone would be doing out on the mesa on such a cold one. When I saw you again this morning, I knew there must be trouble. And I thought you'd want some coffee on a morning like this."

Well, I couldn't contain the wide reaches of my ecstasy. I rushed forward and, to the rancher's straight shock, gave him the biggest hug my arms could afford, enjoying the sandpaper feeling of his beard on my forehead.

"Thank you. Thank you."

His shock turned to amusement. He laughed in the same plodding manner of his speech and patted me on the back.

"All right, all right," J.R. told me. "Give the man some space."

J.R. told Kurt what was wrong with the bus.

"I'll help you out," said Kurt, "though I'm staunchly opposed to the wanton use of oil." He pointed to the ugly puddle, and wouldn't you know all the while, his truck idled behind him like a bad cough. If life isn't a broken mirror glued together by paradox, I don't know what it is.

"Yeah, well, we're staunchly opposed to needless work, so I guess everyone has their passions," I countered.

Kurt laughed in a way that made me think I'd passed a test.

"Well, if you've got a rope, I think I know who could help you out."

J.R. presented our trusty red hammock strap with a great flourish. He tethered it firmly between Sunshine and the Dodge.

As we swayed around the corners, towed by that big truck and drinking our sugary coffee, America impishly peeked over the truck's tailgate.

"For purple mountain's majesty!" she shouted.

She made such a commotion, I'm sure Kurt knew she was back there in the snow-dusted bed. The telltale softness in his eyes was visible in the rearview mirror. As he towed us into Questa, home of the brave, America giggled and threw snowballs at Sunshine, her way of telling us it would all be okay, even through the perilous fight of winter, so long as Optimism prevailed.   ◊

A Simple Act of Providence

By some miracle, we survived winter, limping through those cold months on a small farm in Clark County, Nevada. We worked long days of liberating strife from January through March, digging holes for fence posts, weeding radishes, birthing goats, butchering roosters.

The desert sun beat on our hair and bleached streaks of it white as the warm milk we squirted from the udders of the goats. My hands thickened with calluses. I was in charge of feeding the chickens and collecting their speckled blue eggs. There must have been two hundred of them, and I knew each of their caws and calls.

J.R. and I, we worked every damn day of the week, planting tomatoes and harvesting chard and eating asparagus from a patch near the bus. We learned how to tell if a goat was in rut and how to butcher a pig. We made our own cheese and saved seeds and never had clean fingernails, not for one second.

The first day of spring smelled like a green tomato. We bid goodbye to Dottie and Daria, our two favorite goats in the herd. We cried as we stroked their coarse hair. Leaving them was leaving behind a part of ourselves. We were those tomatoes, that milk, that soil.

We pocketed a wad of cash from Red Rooster Farm and wound our way north along the back roads. That paycheck would carry us to the summer, and we felt like foxes out of the coop. Our spirits soared above us, rooted firmly in the weight of our physical bodies so they wouldn't float away.

We washed our bloody-chicken overalls at a laundromat in Pioche. The television channel was dubbed in Spanish. A cooking show with a laugh track. RV commercials. Flights to Peru. Toys. Fast food. We laughed at each one. We knew better. We didn't need any of that stuff. It wouldn't help us find Tangerine Hot Springs.

North we continued, Ely, Jackpot, Pocatello, Big Sky, Anaconda. These are the names of my home, the corners of America that shelter me from the mundane. Oh beautiful for pilgrimed feet whose stern impassioned stress a thoroughfare of freedom beat across the wilderness! America! America! God mend thine every flaw. Confirm thy soul in self-control, thy liberty by law!

◊ ◊ ◊ ◊

Our second encounter with the Great MacGuffin proved to be the most fortunate fluke of our whole hobo lives.

We stopped at one of those gas stations off the freeway—you know the kind, with big semis humming out front and cigarette butts crushed into the ground, ready to be fossilized into tomorrow's museum specimens and a guy outside wearing a denim outfit, holding a sign saying "Afghanistan Will Not Be Forgotten" or something like that.

There, in the bustling parking lot, was his unforgettable orange VW, Tangerine, sagging under the weight of its heavy solar technology. MacGuffin sat inside the dark cave of his bus like the wizard he was, surrounded by his kingdom of material possessions. Why, MacGuffin could barely wedge his thin frame inside, the poor VW's guts were so jam-packed. He was running twice as many gadgets as the year before, a fridge, a freezer, hand dryer, a CB radio. He even had an E-Lover, which winked at us when we looked inside.

He surveyed our dirty fingernails and tangled hair with a vague smile, as though we'd met thousands of times before but he couldn't quite place our faces.

I marched straight up to the Great MacGuffin and squeezed that wizard in a giant hello hug that could've collapsed a lung.

"It is so good to see you, MacGuffin," I said. "You don't know how often we've called upon your wisdom the past year."

He hummed a small tune in response, as though we were robins and had no use for English anymore. Then he patted me on the head and placed on my forehead a kiss that dripped like rainy season in June.

He held up a photo of himself taking a photo of himself.

"I'm the third coming of Christ. Being a Messiah sure is nice."

"I know," said J.R. "You don't know how many times your name has filtered through my ears the past year."

J.R. presented the rope of licorice he was eating like it was a rosary and Mother

Dumpster was lurking somewhere nearby.

"You are the searchers and seekers," said MacGuffin.

"Thank God we are!" I said. "A most dignified term."

"You are the sinners and preachers!"

"I guess you could put it that way," said J.R.

A cop pulled beside MacGuffin's bus, at that slow pace police assume when they know it's their job to talk to you but really, they'd rather be anywhere else in the world.

"Hello, folks," said the cop, trying his best to treat us like a normal tourist group looking for the local ice cream shop. "I'm going to have to ask you to finish your business patronizing the station and move on. We received a complaint about loitering, which is prohibited in the City of Las Vegas proper."

"Well, Orange Is Optimism," said MacGuffin. "A bum can't even park without seeing a shark."

"Dumpster bread's stale and the government reads our mail," said J.R.

"What a shocker, Uncle Sam rides a walker!" I chimed in.

"What's all this nonsense about?" The officer twisted his brain trying to figure out if we'd insulted him or not, which obviously we hadn't because it was all hobo code, and he couldn't possibly know the vile lawless mysteries of hobo code.

"You think this is nonsense?" I asked. "Oh, man, can we show you nonsense. We can show you all the nonsense you might need to survive. But not right now, okay? My compadre J.R. and I, we're sort of busy over here with our saint and sage MacGuffin, so if you'll excuse us, please—"

"Ma'am, I don't think you quite understand," said the cop. "I ask that you all pack up your possessions—" he gestured to the veritable yard sale we had created "—and shortly be on your way, perhaps to your hometown. Perhaps forever."

"Jefferson's dead and all cops are heads," said MacGuffin, placing the remainder of his vegan hot dog into a plastic Tupperware container. Then he calmly walked around to the driver's side of his bus.

"Homelessness isn't really welcomed around here," the cop continued.

"See, you've got it wrong! We are homeowners. You're looking at our residences right over there." I pointed to Sunshine and then to MacGuffin's orange bus Tangerine, heavy with its suit of solar panels.

"Exactly as I thought." The cop sighed heavily. "I may need to call for backup."

"No, officer, no need to take action," I said, following the lead of the Great MacGuffin and returning to the safety of Sunshine.

"Don't worry about a thing and follow me to Tangerine Hot Springs," MacGuffin called to us from the driver's seat of Tangerine.

Was he really going to take us there? Tangerine Hot Spring, the object of my desire. How could it be that we would finally lay eyes on it? The anticipation alone bored holes through the tiny bones of my hands and vertebrae.

Whether or not MacGuffin was serious, it was time to split. That creaky old truck stop didn't have a speck of life in it. There was nothing for us there, not a glimmer of Freedom or of wildness, just big metal cages around everything.

"Best of luck. Never start giving a fuck!" MacGuffin blew the cop a kiss.   ◊

We sat there, lost

in the timeless void of neverending being

TANGERINE HOT SPRINGS

We embarked on an overland journey to Tangerine Hot Springs, the place of hobo dreams brought to fruition, coughing in the thick smoke of MacGuffin's oil leak wake. He led us to a beautiful dirt back road just where the concrete disaster of Las Vegas fell from the edge of the desert and into a burning pit of electronic coin slots.

When you drive through the neon city, you better be either stupidly messed up on some sort of vile and technically illegal substance, or you better squint your eyes past all the intolerable shining signs and flashes of color. We did a little of both and soon we were freed, unleashed of our urban afflictions and roaming the wide, open deserts that stretched for miles ahead.

We hurtled across the creosote flats, over crooked roads that carved cracks through valleys of fire and past ravens on the wing, croaking in ecstasy, and all the while, the white light of the desert surrendered itself to the ground.

Wild horses galloped across the expanse of land, and I almost cried watching them, knowing I was a human and they were horses and what was the difference between us anyway. I popped my head out the open window, freer than free, because not one person in the world beside J.R. and MacGuffin knew where I was right then. That must be the most delicious knowledge in the whole world.

Our journey continued for miles and minutes, then hours and days.

Finally, we arrived at a river, a genuine oasis in the pink rock desert. Near its shores was a flat place to park and a fire ring stocked with dry dead branches. We cooked a big breakfast over the coals in the 6 a.m. light. We finished our meal, but didn't move an inch. The sky was an arched watermelon peel. It was impossible to look away, because it's not every day the sky turns into fruit salad.

Time became an accessory to everything evil. At one point, I saved the Great MacGuffin from a near death. He went to look at his wristwatch, and just in time I slapped him across the face. What was wrong with him? Was he was a fool? Didn't he know the face of that watch would inject him with venom if we wasn't careful?

Silence overtook us, for five minutes, three hours, thirty one days. We just kept sitting there, lost in the timeless void of never-ending being.

In a quantum leap, J.R. dropped his underwear and bolted into the river, jumping and splashing and swimming like a river dolphin through the swift current. Eternity cracked right in half when he pulled that stunt.

MacGuffin and I joined him in the turquoise waters. Together, as a devoted threesome of pilgrims, we cleansed ourselves of our road grime. In and out of the river our buoyant bodies slipped, a regular baptism, and oh boy, don't you believe the water, like ink, could splat and splitter and blot out all of our iniquity? And oh boy, don't you think sinners like us could use a dose of redemption every morning?

America, I pray that God shed his grace on thee as you float down these clean blue waters looking for Sanity.

Optimism, I pray that God bless you, happy and free.

J.R. and I finished our bath, only to observe that the third head of our orange trinity, the Great MacGuffin, had vanished.

We wandered downstream, investigating the underside of every river stone for any small sign of MacGuffin, because he seemed like someone who might up and transform into a frog. A tinkle of laughter rippled in orange waves from a cluster of reeds. When we emerged from the dense grasses, we strolled through the pearly gates of hot spring heaven.

My poor eyes. They abandoned their sockets and orbited my empty head like the lumpy rings of Saturn.

There it bubbled, righteous before us undeserving bums, sacred before us sinning seekers. Tangerine Hot Springs. Every detail MacGuffin mentioned, down to the most minuscule toenail on the foot of Uncle Sam, was there. Its palatial waters comfortably housed MacGuffin, J.R., and me with plenty of space for Optimism and Freedom. Oh, and of course, America too, but she kept getting out and picking fruit from the nearby orchards, mixing it with wine and offering us sangria.

Oh beautiful for glory's sake, how do I describe Tangerine Hot Springs? Would you believe that in its waters, God mended my every flaw?

Sometimes I wish I could speak in colors or scents. Words can be so constricting. Like, how do I describe its sheer unbearable perfection, its sensual delight of mineral majesty? Ah. I wish I could, but I wouldn't know how to tell you. The water massaged my skin and that light…did you see that light?! It floated down onto me and the cholla and the whole earth, in fact, from the endless depths of history, still warm even after that long journey.

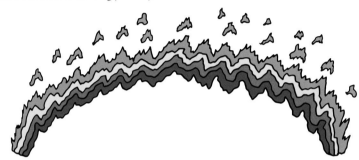

We soaked in the orgasm waters of the hot spring as though the day was eternal and every god that ever existed shone its benevolence onto us. At one point in the late afternoon, when the air had just begun its daily discussion with evening about the fate of the world, I heard a voice. It galloped through the air like the tiniest jockey on the most elegant racehorse.

"That's Sanity," said MacGuffin. "She comes by for a chat every time I soak."

"I knew she wasn't dead," I said.

"Nonsense. Who would tell you something as crazy as that?"

"Everyone in America," I said.

MacGuffin turned to the grasses where Sanity's voice whinnied.

"Come on over, goddess! You know the water's fine."

Sanity stepped from the reeds, wearing a red and white striped skirt with a bronze plate over her torso. She approached Tangerine Hot Springs, and the entire world paused in her presence. Was she a ghost? Alive? I couldn't tell you.

I *can* tell you one thing. I know this sounds fantastical, but you've got to believe that right there in that hot spring, Sanity scooped us up and cradled us in her arms.

It was realer than anything that's ever happened to me. In fact, if I was forced to believe in truth based on any incident that's occurred firsthand in my own life, I would choose that very afternoon when Sanity brushed my hair out of my eyes in the bubbling waters of Tangerine Hot Springs.

The fiery day froze into a ice cream sundae evening. We told raw bleeding secrets with Sanity and MacGuffin as a diamond night carved its way overhead. When our eyes turned to sandpaper, we swam the moonlit waters of the river back to camp. Sanity watched us, then retired to her refuge in the reeds.

J.R. stoked up the bonfire from breakfast, and it soon spoke its language of energy. We huddled around it, amazed that we could illuminate the night with pieces of recycled sun. Silence blanketed us for a few dozen crackles from the fire. We were still as oil paintings in a defunct museum.

"It was a good day," said MacGuffin.

"It was *the* day," I said. "Today we found Tangerine Hot Springs."

"Yes," said MacGuffin. "Today and only today."

"What do you mean?" I asked.

"Well, pilgrims, you must understand. You may visit the holy land, but you cannot remain here."

"What do you mean?"

"Surely you didn't expect to stay. This is no place to take up residence. Every honest seeker eventually finds that which they seek. However, you must remember that every goal is fleeting, much like life itself. No revelation can endure more than a few moments of scrutiny, lest it transmute its power and glory into the mundane."

"But I don't understand."

"You must leave tomorrow pilgrims," said MacGuffin. "I'm sorry to say it."

"Where will we go?"

"There is nothing to do but to enjoy your moment of ecstasy and get on with the rest of existence."

I wept like the shortest verse in the Bible. J.R. lit a cigarette.

"Now, now, seekers," said MacGuffin. "You know there's no truth, and what thoughts can disturb you after you've realized something as horrific as that?"

MacGuffin slept out under the stars that evening, claiming there were too many machines in his bus to enjoy a proper night's sleep there. We propped open our door too, for the breeze and for any chance of capturing divine inspiration.

I didn't open a groggy eye until the sun was high and hot and the birds sought shelter under the cottonwood trees. I'd slept like a sinner forgiven. It was a regular Canyonlands morning, a golden eagle on the wing, sunlight on my arms. But

despite the morning's warm welcome, a vacuous yearning ached in my abdomen.

MacGuffin had vanished like a dream. We searched the tumbleweed-infested margins of the road for any evidence of his exit, but we found nothing. No tire tracks. No telltale pee puddles. No electronic waste. Even the fire ring was gone.

"I knew that guy was a trope," said J.R.

"I bet MacGuffin went back to Tangerine Hot Springs. I bet he's over there now."

"Anything's possible. Probably not probable. "

"It can't be true that we have to leave. We just found it. We just met Sanity."

"They say it's all downhill from hello, Kit."

"J.R., let's live here. Let's build a little cabin over by those reeds. Sanity will be our neighbor and we'll soak in the springs every single day."

"You never stop with the delusions, do you?"

"Delusions are the raw materials of Optimists. Out of them, we create reality."

We crossed the Turquoise River. The reeds were thick as before and we struggled through their tangled barrier. When we parted the matted grasses, I held my breath, anticipating the scene we had encountered the day before.

Gone were the warm thermal waters. Gone were the trees of stone fruit and cherries. Gone were the beautiful songbirds. Gone were the skies that leaked tangerine light. It was just river, river, as far as we could see.

I supposed MacGuffin was right. Truth is capricious and epiphanies fade fast.

Back at Sunshine, we found an antique cigar box that smelled like Thomas Jefferson. Inside was a photo of J.R. taking a photo of MacGuffin at Tangerine Hot Springs. It was taped to a sheet of folded orange paper.

PILGRIMS,

I HAVE ANOTHER QUEST IN MIND FOR YOU. YOUR NEW DESTINY AWAITS: RAINBOW FALLS.

UNDER ITS THUNDEROUS SPRAY, YOU MAY BE CLEANSED OF THE AFFLICTION OF WORK AND GIVEN A NEW LIFE OF LEISURE AND IDLENESS.

IN THE MOSSES AND FERNS OF RAINBOW FALLS, SANITY HAS DECIDED TO TAKE UP RESIDENCE. I ENCOURAGE YOU TO DEVOTE YOUR TRAVELS TO HER PURSUIT.

NEVER FORGET, PERFECTION CAN ONLY BE ENCOUNTERED IN SMALL DOSES.

ORANGE IS OPTIMISM.

—THE GREAT MACGUFFIN

I quit my pathetic crying. J.R. bit into a pickle. We exchanged grins and wild-sounding yawps. Renewed with vigor by the holy message of MacGuffin, determined to discover the healing waters of Rainbow Falls and her caretaker Sanity, we dashed down the road, laughing like Insanity had taken a century-long vacation to the Andromeda Galaxy.

◊ ◊ ◊ ◊

We're somewhere in nowhere, Utah right now. Westward bound, the yellow dotted lines running into each other like an ancient spiritual text.

You know, even after our dreamy encounter a few days back, I can't definitively say we found Sanity at Tangerine Hot Springs. It might have been her ghost, considering she's taken up residence at Rainbow Falls. It might've been Lady Liberty, for all we knew. It wasn't Capitalism in disguise, though. That much was for sure.

Just this morning, I caught a glimpse of a small figure moving through the sage. Could've been a jackrabbit, I suppose, but I'd like to think it was Sanity herself, that she's with been with us this whole time and that one day, she'll come out of hiding for good, just like Optimism did.

So there's that hope. J.R. and I, we won't give up our search, no matter what. A proper journey never ends and there's no capital-T "There" to aim for. Never ever forget that, dear reader. I know I try not to, especially in dark times when it seems the imperialism of Insanity is too mighty to overthrow.

It's not always easy out here on the road, trying to escape our own madness and the madness of everyone in those megacities. Sometimes it's lonely out here, being an Optimist, because forging a friendship with Optimism was a bold action for us to take. Everyone talks about Optimism like she's a surgeon known for botched lobotomies. That's a bunch of bullshit.

Here's something only a bum could tell you. Once you follow the laws of Optimism, once you focus on the beautiful abundance around you, you become the most radical radical there is. And happy to boot.

Sometimes it seems America's divided and everyone thinks Pessimism will glue her back together. Sometimes everyone hangs out with Pessimism, like I used to do, complaining in their madness that they're Americans but that they're not proud to be Americans. Ah, that old symptom of Insanity.

Me? I love America. She provides a chance to find Sanity, and that chance is equal for all. You can be whoever you want and America will still show up to your party, and for that I salute her.

I'm grateful for Freedom, too. Because of her, we aren't bound to any one place. We aren't held ransom by routine. We're wide open with only the white lines on the side of the highway to hold us in and keep us from spilling out all over the place.

And Optimism? She's still in our back seat working her alchemy, telling us to keep on it, because what's the good in giving up when nowhere is the most beautiful place you can be?

In Optimism we trust, and by Optimism may we never arrive, because a proper journey never ends.

So we're off, following the rainbow roads of the Arizona Strip, continuing on because that's the only thing we know how to do. We'll be out there, in the mountains and the prairies and the oceans white with foam forever, giving thanks to the land which gave us birth. We'll wander the open roads of America till we die, armed with honesty and dignity and not much else.

Really, when it all comes down to it, we've got nothing but joy and anticipation, and maybe that's all we'll ever have. Hey, that's a tank of gas and good map for an Optimist. It's a kick in the rear end, sending us on our merry way down the cracked and beckoning road. We'll take it and hope we keep seeing orange all our lives, because all the colors matter, but Orange is Optimism. ◊

WE'VE
GOT
NOTHING
BUT JOY
AND
ANTICIPATION
AND
MAYBE
THAT'S ALL
WE NEED

The End

Supporters

Peace Vans
Harley Sitner
Rob Kearney

Jim Kraemer
Stephen Porter
Alex Nason
Laurent Lathieyre
Mykll Valiant
Robert
Pine Key
Jeff & Selene Gribble
Alex Roodhouse
Marji Kilgus
Daniel Kodsi
Ami Seener
Timothy
Amber Pennington
Joerg Jasper
Phil Rowley
Megan DeLay
André Kramer
Steven DeLay
Louis Skipper
Pierre-Antoine Moelo
Justin Burger
Eric Deterding
Tom Martin
Thomas Welch
Kirsten Niesar
Rob Munz
Olivia Crescenti
Shirley Hampshire
Cal Hyland
Richard Robertson
Laren Campbell
Hannah Heitman
Brett Van Emst
Sarah Horton-Campbell
Pam Bolton
Scooter Gabel
Legendary-Jakten
Janine Holt
Brock Butterfield
Carissa Fullon
Lode Behaeghe
Dan
Chris Nolan
Rachael Blondy
Allen Yuricic
Ted Grubb
Soulier Pierre-alain
Michael Moore
Keith Ludwig
Rich
Steve Schmidt

Jay Roberts
elizabeth lee pasko
Steven Caskey
Scott Good
Nerissa Nicholls
Ramsey Alexander III
Anafrancesca Comunale
Brittany Comunale
Jacob Simmons
Connor A. Cunningham
Mathew Holt
Luke Ludeman
Don
WJ van den Eijkhof
Nicholas Schoeder
Mathias Lynders
Cody Pickren
Michael Henschke
Gregoire Bolduc
Ryan Snyder
Steven Goldfarb
Willow Reyes
Rebecca Ray
Joseph Borkovic
Zach Borkovic
Tracey Goldfarb
Tulpin Francis
Scott
Michael Olsen
Hans Mayer
Kevin Ryan
Whit Haynes
Cynthia Langford
Jessica Edelen
Bruce Lipsky
Brent
Ronnie McCaskill
Allie Arnfield
Jackson Hawkins
David Temkin
Hien Temkin
Loneoutdoorsman
Hayden Morris
Amanda Ciesielczyk

D. Hill
Kevin Bradburn
Michael Kayson
Scott Wilhelm
Jonathan Aaron Southwood
Chris
S
Cheri Cole
Martin Veverka
Melanie Margolis
Ramsay Bell

Justin Briasco
Sandro Mingardi
Nils Langloh
Kaley Mays Chapman
Peter Eich
Socrates Gliarmis
Michael Groothuis
Amy Pickell
Michael Machbert
Katie
Ali Spackman
Robert Cooney
Falon Cartwright
Nicole Parker
Jamie F.
Steve Pendarvis
Hannelore Inman
Scott Anson
Jane Bell
Catherine Miller
Gaspard Gasparov
Mathias Møller Jespersen
Bob HawleyW
Ron Humphrey
Elizabeth Van Hest
Marilyn Johnson
Terry Johnson
Judith
David Perrott
Janet Valesares
Crystal
Darrell Marks
Edwin E Plummer Jr
Patrik Henriksson
Cory O'Shea
Matt
Dennis van Meurs
Donna Crawford
Mark Bristow
Carsten Fulland
Thomas Hadinger
Joe Sabolchic
Kevin Richardson
Patrick Jost
Mark Weber
Joanne Deshpande
Sophia Chia Min Yi
Katie
Federico
James Ley
Stu Wemhoener
Marci Wemhoener
Rayni Wiggins
Doug Aadland
Theresa Aadland
Elisabeth Herriman
Clarke Gottwald
Yari Weaver
John Spicer
Vina Lustado
Robert Vos

Charles H. Hobson
Niclas Magnusson
Mattias Eriksson
Ryan
William Quinlin
Michael Mitchell
Jason Lightfoot
Eugene Schneider
Richard Stanwix
Simone Stanwix
Velyn Tan

Gail Embree
Jamie Nice
Jonathan
Tudor Oroian
Maddie Murphy
Elizabeth George
Apirak Krishnamra
John McLeod
Vickie McLeod
Lorrie Koenings
Jimi Koenings
Brian Flanagan
Susan Alden
Ricky Tockes
Katie
Davide S
Jon Shoemaker
Jeff Spencer
Sascha Kis
Daniel Certa
Steph
Richard Alexander
Aaron Christensen
Scott Persson
Olivia Sullivan
Beau Matheny
Ryan Hanson
Roman
Einsiedler Florian
Erbig Simona
David Ames
Rich Misicko
Heather
Scott Harrison
Ruth Dukeman
Silvio Luisoni
Jeremiah Pennell
Thomas Chapman
Pascal Nicoulau
Steven Common
Jennifer Day
Michelle
Graham Simon
Blake Fitzpatrick

Ginny Threlkeld
Laura Turner
Jim Miller
Wayne Norman
Jitka Mikulastikova
Matty Caruso
Katie Sullivan
Talia Fletcher
Jonathan Guzman
Tyson Payne
Keith Van Norstrand
Matt Groves
Dave Westhoff
Rick Younker
Brenton Perry
James Lambie
Daniel Leonidas
Sean Leonard
Arthur Hefti
Kristin Boatwright
Ian Redcay
Ramy Lahoud
Nick Turner
Jennifer Wolf
Eddie Abbott
Scalbert Mathieu
Beth Butler
Greg Allin
Martha Watson
Ludovic
Jonathan C. Acuff
Kim, Sonny
Paddlefish Sports
Alden Roth

Rob Leonard
Chris Coffman
Shawn Rawlings
Gus Mojica
John Kates
Katrina Drabeck
Mic Shindle
Michael Wallisch
Jed Hegwood
Amy Hegwood
Martha Noonan
Ian S Glover
Dave Martinez
Stan Leslie
Jon McGaha
Jake Weatherly
Chris Pace
Heather Rhew
Joel Anderson
Bethany Anderson
Brian Hewitt
Kent Griswold

Dubeee
Martin
Kevin McDevitt
Kalle Alajärvi
Skiddy McSquiddy
Martin William Sim
Kristen McDougal
Alan Bezoza
Dan Shear
Sara Lamp-Goodwin
Brad
Michael Quinlan
Josh McDonell
Bryant Nguyen
Steve Deason
Seth Barker
Anna Gaudia
Sandrine Lambert
Keri Whitman
Sam Shirey
Brady
Kate Mullen
Christian Morrison
Julie Gibb
Chanda Baker
Jenny Anderson Haas
Kim Blakeley
Sandy Sanders
Sandra Hovmand
Adélie Audet
Scott basse
Lee Ann Clements
Morgan Brown
John Stuart Hannam
Bethany Barich
Genester
Amanda W
Spence
Katy Lupien
Andrea Monaghan Roberts
Brandon Rogers
Robin Viester
Eve Josephson
Oliver Pritchard
Dave Ireland
Stephan Lamoureux
Chrystal
Jessica Quinn
Ian Quinn
Michael Greer
Megan Jurvis
Cara Giannone
Zach Westendorp
Sam
Daniell
Chad Slater
Diane Wittling
Peter Graessle
Chris Hayward
Diana Hayward
Dwight Busby

Kitchen Wizard
Sierra Kniskern
Bengt F. Weisshuhn
Mike McRoberts
Maria Patterson
Shawn Cissell
Gilad Solter
Chandra Frei
Monnier Tristan
Titouan Fournier
Christine Vintimilla
Matt Sanders
Summer Hayton Silvestri
Max Hoyle
Haileigh Burr
Mercedes Annon
Roxxanne Turner
Bill Radobenko
Sue Radobenko
Chelsey Barber
Sina
Lilly Mansmann
Alexa Bleile
Chris Rose
Eric Benton
Ashley Benton

Henning Kettler
Jared Sturgis
Julie Dean
Jan Löffler
David Walker
Aria Zarnoski
Caroline Durgnat
Jacob Verhesen
Misuuu
Carole Thompson
Daniel Berner
Jim Crews
Kate
Nick Pence
Dan Opalacz
Ben Wakefield
Bobby Moser
Ben Mullinkosson
Elsa
Nate Rogers
Daniel Erlandson
Meghan Talotta
Theresa Lowe
Josh Beatty
Mike Buchholz
Karen Forster
Jenna Newburn
Michelle Monik
Rachel McGlone
Samantha Doolittle
Evgeny Vasenev
Brooke Billings
Chevalier Chris
Be Kind Vibes
Marc Boudreau
Jerry Jaramillo
Cara Marie
Sarah Stonier

Christopher Quesnel
Clemens Zefferer
Emma Versaw
Aidan, Madison, Parker, Joel
Stephanie Reichel
Robert Oliver
Daisy Pavlovics
Steve Barry
Jeff Morgan
Gwen Wurm
Andrew Hawthorne
Rosanna Harkin
Wild We Wander
Steven McKay
Michael Gabriel
J. Hayes
Pete W.
Jennifer Carvallo
Seth
Chris Brown
West Trekking
Jessica
Susan Langdon
Kerry Francis
Janette
Kathleen, Greg, Blaize
Christina Menchini
Oliver
Art Bikes
Scott Lukesh
Kristyn Rautenbach
Liz
Sam Lafrenière
Brooke Stoker
Vicki Walker
Heather Fisher
Erin Krutz
V. Line
Ulrich Graf-Nottrodt
Doug W.
Dane
Anthony Laskowsky
Dieter Bussche
Adam Browne
Mark DeLorenzo
Nat Brown
Jerimiah
Louise Putterill
James
Carly
Amy Gerhard
Casey Jones
Veronica Naomi Valliere
Steven D. Johnson
Christa Kongs
Renee Purcell
Matthew Koons
Jay Jacoby
Adam Sauerwein
Julien Christin
Anterra
Ken Marchant
Kyce Bello
Bonnie Moore
Jim Haugh
Amber
Kiki
Gina Peters
Michael Rady

Derek Tremain
Liam Bainton
Mark Straby
Heather Rhen
Juliette
Craig McCurdy
Shannon Palmer
Chris Harrison
Sean Woodworth
Bruce Sherman
Gary Karasek
Ayanna Karasek
Gaylon Watson
Emily Hinton
Mark Morel
Trevor Herndon
Ian Horgan
Moshe Rivel
Jonas Wurster
Elizabeth Johnson
Emily Unruh
Gianluca Tedesco
Dottie Greene
Sven Bollenbach
Jordan Buell
Matthew Stover
Andrea Laue
Kiran Nimmagadda
Danielle Menteer
Jack Beidler
Kodie Lentz
Matthew Madlem
Peter Childs
Nicola (deleted)
Michael Cohen
Livewell
Brent Holoviak
Morgan Biggs
Marco
James Bennett
Lars Reber
Leah Jost
James D Phenicie
Natasha Penaguiao
Stefanie Feichtner
Holly Stephans

Tatrawee Harikul
Jennifer Bakos
Margaux
Sarah Barker
Mike Whitcraft
Steve Davis
Jennaka
Margaret Hayes
Morten
Chris
Angi Hale
Jason Neuman
Ailie McDonald
Pia Harrison
Margaret Winiarczyk
Thibaut Jossein

Tyler Halvorsen
Alex Gulsby
Jeanette Stokes
Simone Mul-Baker
Filip
Landon Holbert
Rory Radovich
Sarah K. Lambino
Jeffrey Anderson
Tara
Elise Brianne
Megan
Sean Thornley
Sarah Brennan
Benjamin Kock
Madeline Finnegan
Simon
Sam MacKay
Feral Watches
Duncan Goad
Bill Thomas
David Leonard
Brittany Waldron
Tal Sapoznikov
Paco G.
Scott Cardinali
Victor Hernandez
Jonathan Papich
Charles De Valois
Alan Reece
Boutoille-Blois
Yann Grobon
Margaret Ryan
Quivogne
Stacy Slattery
John Slattery
Scott Waters
Jason Pawela
Jasmine Maclean
Vincent DiResta
Ron Bureta
Etchegoin
Allison Potts
Jordan Wilson
Shane Coggins
Sam Douthat
Jared Planter
Cary Telander Fortin
Jason Rowe
Bachofen Rolf
James
Nicolas Swicord
Slow Travel Magazine
Aaron
Norm Pure
Nicholas Cahill
Karina Beanato
Chad Harmon
Jennifer Eckenrode
Jared
Slosse Caroline
Julien Eko
Tiffany Eberhardt
Victoria Petrocelli
Laura
Alexander Hofmann
Justin Bussieres
Cheri Jones
Julian Horne
Victoria Stahl

Arthur Brown
Jacqueline Perez
Klemens
Victor Tilley
Kelly Reich
Todd Bolstad
Jack Alexander
Cathy White Thompson
Summer Caton
Sabrina Shamma

Jason Lyga
Sayde
Michael Rountree
Guillaume Brs
Maarten Delanghe
Katie Harhen
Liam McGivney
Megan Sargent
Caleb Foster
Matthew Morey
Mike Ricci
Stephanie Barnes
Ari
Tina Jones
Valentino Joel
Rita
Tommaso Pini
Nathan Corkhill
Aleece Case
Samantha Koehler
Seth Glingle
B. P. Anderson
Stephen Whitney
Adam Harteau
Amy Wagner
Alec Brochhausen
Andrew
Kazden
Loren Threlkeld
Veronica Dombroski
Greg
Martinus Cox Bianchin
Christina K.
Matt McKeon
Frank
Polly & Mark Stoker
Julie
Scott Carolan
Ryan Ramrod Nyquist
Cole Netten
D. J. Polzin
Dawn bennett
Harry Rees Parkes
Madison Abernethy
Heino Felder
Dale Warren
Jason Duncan
Erin Robb
Deanna Stringer
Heather Harris
Kasey Forshey
Joel Bowder
David Israel II

Afton
Emma Larson
Molly Fleet
Scott Hillman
Anna Lasche Acton
Noah Compton
Gloriant Phil
Massimiliano
Anna Watkins
Rob Paquet
Peter Prismall
Gian Marco Melito
Marie Salindre
Gerard Hammond
Zindel
Robin Von Schwarz
Julien Bacus
Josanne
Anna Van Buskirk
James Stuart
Amanda Syryda
Patrick Marchand
Matt Barton
Daniel
Rob Irvine
Horst Kaletsch
Liz Harvey
Dominique DiNome
Eliza Soroka
Kate Danielsen
Andrea Cox
Liane Taffa
Gray Amick
Matthew Wood
Chris Fowlie
Hannah James
Gaby Thomas
Kaylee Nauta
Ruth Russell
Towing Home
Bret Lanius
Lindsey
Stacie Mercer
Karen Johnson
Claude
Hannah Gibbs
Maia Boorer
Brittanie Leibold
Jainee Dial
Lindsey Elliott
Martha A. Belury
Angie Clarke
Part Play
Sammie
Tricia Comins
Bryan Fuss
Gonçalo Paiva Pona
Alyssa Akkoul
Charles Bouldin
Mogli
Jeanne Sarton Du Jonchay
Landry Océane
Adrea Knox
Matthew Baxter
Treasure
Ken Bolden
Dara & Julian Rajeshwar
Barry Dawson

kit Whistler

Kit is a writer and illustrator with an affinity for the absurd. She is also the creator of Rainbow Realism and a firm believer in the redemption of the road. She spends her days running wild.

www.kitWhistler.com
@KitWhistler

J.R. Switchgrass

J.R. captures every moment in his light tight box. It's how he looks at the world. He makes videos too, with a penchant for conceptual documentary. You can see his work here:

www.JRSwitchgrass.com
@JRSwitchgrass

That's All

Thanks for joining us on a wild ride across America, and for exploring concepts of idle theory through the high altitudes of the mind. It has been a pleasure and we hope that now you leave this book armed to enjoy a bit of idleness. Remember, there is great joy in doing nothing. Take some time for it every day. Hope to see you out on the road. All our love.

get on the bus

www.IdleTheoryBus.com

🔲 @IdleTheoryBus

f @IdleTheoryBus